Manny Shirazi was born in Iran in 1946 and was a teacher there for five years. She first published a feminist short story at the age of twelve. She has had both prose and poetry published in Farsi (Persian) and continues to write in Farsi. She is a photographer and held an exhibition of photographs of Women in Iran at the Women's Arts Alliance in 1979; she is an active anti-racist feminist, committed to Women's Liberation in the Third World.

MANNY SHIRAZI

Javady Alley

 The Women's Press

To the young girls of Iran, hoping they too will
remember the past in constructing the future

First published by The Women's Press Limited 1984
A member of the Namara Group
124 Shoreditch High Street, London E1 6JE

British Library Cataloguing in Publication Data

Shirazi, Manny
 Javady Alley.
 I. Title
 823   PR9507.9.S5

 ISBN 0-7043-3928-5

Typeset by M C Typeset, Chatham, Kent
Printed in Great Britain by Nene Litho
and bound by Woolnough Bookbinding,
both of Wellingborough, Northants

Acknowledgments

I would have liked to have written my first book in Farsi, but as I was unable to I wrote it in English. To be brought up in an Iranian working-class family with no formal English education and then land in London and try to write in English, involved a number of problems, only a few of which were finding the books I needed in British libraries, learning to type and learning to write 'the Queen's English'!

It was a struggle to gain access to books, mainly Iranian books or books on Iran, in British libraries. I was required to produce two British professional references in order to gain access to Iranian books! This demand I found both authoritarian and racist. I thank Irene Brennan and Alec Gordon for becoming my referees.

Many friends, feminists, also women from my local estate, have helped me with their ideas, skills, friendship and financial and spiritual support. Among them are my feminist writers' group, Mitchel, Alison, Pauline, Fiona and Penny who made helpful comments on my first manuscript. I thank Judith, Lorraine Degale, Hilda Bellingham and Steve Farrer for reading and typing parts of the final manuscript. Also thanks to Asphodel, and to the Leonard Cohen Foundation for their grant towards the cost of typing and photocopying the final manuscript. Urvashi Butalia from Zed Press and Ruthie Petrie from Virago, the sisters at The Women's Press and Deborah and Mary from A Woman's Place read the final manuscript and advised me on parts of it. I thank them for their care and concern.

I am thankful to many friends and neighbours who have helped me with babysitting, especially Myra Everett and Alf in Durham who looked after him for most of his school holidays, to give me time to write the book.

I am grateful to my friends Rachel Langton and Helen Ramsbottom, who have burned the midnight oil with me. They have constantly helped me to write, rewrite, type, retype and most of all to correct my 'unqueenly' English.

One of the ideas that helped me throughout the writing of this book was the similarity between the shabby council estate where I live – the isolation of women, violence against women, racism towards non-whites, filth and decay – and the slum conditions in Iran, or any other Third-World Country. I have also learned from my child's ideas and play experiences. The poverty of children in this area, who wait in the laundry for their clothes to be washed and dried before going to school, is similar to that of children in the Third World.

In the process of writing this book I have shared ideas and experiences with white feminists, and I have enjoyed and learned from these; but I am also aware of racism within the Women's Liberation Movement and imperialist attitudes towards struggling women in the Third World, especially since recent events in the Middle East.

I am particularly thankful to Black womens writing against racism. They gave me insights into developing the characters of this book.

I am indebted to the women from the Iranian Women's Group, especially Parizad, who gave me ideas and warm support; and to Iranian women back home who told me their stories. Their courage and resistance has encouraged me to write this book now, although I have had the idea in mind since I was eight.

Manny
January 1984

One

It was the summer of 1953. The days were hot and unbearably long. Morning started with sun spreading and heating the air. We got up with the heat and the day began with Mother plaiting my hair. I sat between her knees, holding on to them with both hands, with my back to her, and leaned on her feet. She combed my hair, wetting it with water, parting it in two and plaiting it on either side of my face behind my ears.

Shaba, my grandmother, also combed and plaited her hair, but only sometimes, not every day like me. She had long hair but it was very thin and its colour was white and grey, not black like mine and Mother's. Mother had long hair but she didn't plait it, just fastened it behind her.

Combing and plaiting my hair was painful, it pulled and made my head ache. I didn't like it, but Father liked long hair for girls and women and didn't want me to have my hair cut.

I was sitting in the shade in our yard. It was late afternoon but the air hadn't cooled yet. It was still hot and sweat was gathering behind my ears where my plaited hair started. We were waiting for Father to come home from his factory so we could eat our supper. I wanted to go out and wait in the lane but I was afraid that he would tell me off. Whenever I saw him in the street, I would run home and try to hide in a corner.

I was sitting and waiting. Father's bus must have stopped in the square by now. He must be on his way home.

We lived in the south of Tehran near the railway station, the only railway station in the city. It was a huge, white, wide marble building, built by the Germans and by far the most impressive building in the area. It stood on the north side of Railway Square, a small and continuously overcrowded place where the city bus run ended, and the taxis waited.

Immediately surrounding the railway were the city slums, housing the working class, the unemployed, and the homeless casual migrant workers who slept in the wasteland behind the council estate.

In the middle of Railway Square there was a small green fenced-off patch with neatly planted red roses and geraniums. In the midst of the flowers stood a large, grey marble column that supported a huge bronze statue of the Shah sitting on a galloping horse. He was holding the horse's reins in one hand, and waving with the other.

Three long, wide roads led out from Railway Square. To the left was a straight, busy road lined on either side with shops. This was the trading centre for men's garments, always full of people bargaining. To the right, the road curved over a narrow stone bridge that spanned a wide river. The river – black with sewage from the north and full of rubbish – was the dividing line between the north and south of Tehran. Before the bridge, the road was covered with fruit stalls and street kitchens on either side: a thriving open-air market. Opposite the station there was a long straight road leading to the north, along which a bus route ran, right down Pahlavi Avenue and past the Shah's Winter Palace, to the hills of Shimran and his Summer Palace.

Between the eastern and the northern roads there was a small park with some green grass and wooden benches. A couple of hundred yards away from Railway Square there was a chain of tortuous alleys, one leading into another, and we lived right at the bottom of this maze. Our house was the last door in a row of three in the last, tiny, dead-end alley. This alley led to a wider alley which in turn led to an intersection of alleys, one of which had an outlet on to a road. There was a grocery, bakery and a fruiterer on this road, and cars could pass through.

Our house faced the end of the wider alley, called Javady Alley. It was a small two-bedroom brick house of two storeys, with a wooden front door. Through the door there was a large yard with a hoze, a little pond, in the middle. There were two rooms on each floor, and we lived on the ground floor. One room was our sitting room and bedroom, the other was a guest room which was always locked. In the yard under the staircase were a toilet and kitchen next to each other. It wasn't our house, we were tenants of my mother's step-mother who lived in the two rooms above us. She was the third wife, but when Mother's father married another, younger woman, she got a divorce, and came down to Tehran with her son

Shapor to live on her own.

Our sitting room was square, with two small rugs covering the floor. There was a bundle of bedding at one side of the room, and a large trunk with tea plates and a samovar at the other: the bare necessities, nothing decorative. But on the mantelpiece there were some photos: one of my father's sister and her children who lived in the Soviet Union, one of my mother with her grandmother and her step-mother and step-brother. All the women had hats on: at that time, I was told, women weren't allowed to wear the chador.

I got tired of waiting in the yard so I went to the living room and started playing five-stones. My mother was sitting on the floor, bending over a tray full of rice, searching through it to clean out the grit. She looked up and called me.

'You know, Homa, I'm taking you to a girls' school tomorrow to register your name. Your birthday is coming up. You will be seven years old in Mordad [August], it's time you began school. We'll enrol you now, before the end of term, so that you will have a place and can begin in Mehr [October].'

I nodded with joy. How exciting to go to a new place to meet new people! I felt shy and nervous – such a big change. I wanted to get out of the house. I wanted to say something, to ask questions, but I didn't. I began to think and dream about it.

Father walked in and threw the daily paper on the carpet. The bold letters of the headlines leapt out at us. A moment later he picked it up again and read them out loud:

DEMONSTRATIONS AGAINST BP IN TEHRAN

MOSADEGH'S NATIONAL GOVERNMENT ON VERGE OF COLLAPSE

FRENCH RAID ON INDO-CHINA

3000 BRITISH TROOPS AND SAS DEFOREST MALAYAN COMMUNISTS' HIDEOUT

HUSBAND BURNS ALIVE ADULTEROUS WIFE IN SHIRAZ

Nobody took any notice.

Father was a very tall man; he had to bend down when coming through the door. He was always frowning, and looked very serious. A quick sharp 'salam', and he would sit on the floor, take off his shoes, throw his socks in the corner. They would be wet with sweat, and stink. He would call out to my mother, 'Mina, is the hot water ready?' as he took off his overalls and threw them in the corner too. Then he would put on his soft cotton pyjamas. Mother appeared with a bowl of hot water, a towel on her arm, and some soap in her hand. She bent down and put the water near his feet, and he put them in the warm water and took a deep, soothing breath. Next she gave him the soap, and he washed the sweat and the dirt off his feet and toes. She held the towel on her arm, half bending, and waited with her hands folded. With the hanging towel folded neatly over them, she looked like a wooden towel holder. When he had finished washing his feet, she handed him the towel, bent to take the dirty water, stinking socks and filthy overall, and carried them through the doorway into the yard, where she had to wash them.

'Homa, give me a glass of water,' he calls out to me. 'The dinner is ready,' Shaba calls. He disappears behind his newspaper while Grandma is preparing the dinner. She always does the cooking. She spreads the sofreh (the cotton cloth we eat off); and puts the plates on it. Only when the food comes in does he reluctantly put the paper down. It must be a good day, there is food to eat and it is abgosht, the traditional working-class meal. It is stew made of meat, chickpeas, potatoes, tomatoes and sour spices. He likes this dish very much. 'Mmm, good food,' he calls out.

He likes preparing and dishing it out. First he pours some gravy out into a big bowl; then he chops some bread into small pieces, puts them in the gravy, mixes it all up, and when it is well soaked he shares it out, one portion for my brother and me with our mother, one portion shared with his mother. After the first course is finished, he pours the rest of the stew into the same bowl and mashes it all up together before eating it with bread. He holds the masher firmly and brings it down on the peas and meat and smashes them to pieces. With every beat the ingredients move around and are ground up; crushed and crushed until they are softened and mixed up, ready to be eaten. This mashing is a man's job. He has the strength to do it, and with some show of power and pleasure he does it while women wait on him.

Father always reminded us that he was the breadwinner, even at supper-time. He prepared the food the way he wanted it, and he divided it between us. He always kept the best and largest part himself, unless he was with men friends, or wanted to be generous to us.

4

'Afagh asked about the rent arrears,' Shaba whispered, hoping that the respect due to the meal would restrain him from exploding into curses.

'Fuck her, she must wait until next week. Fucking woman, she isn't desperate – she has piles of money anyway.'

A heavy silence fell through the rest of the meal.

I didn't like abgosht. I didn't like the way it was prepared and eaten. Everything mixed, so we missed the taste of each separate ingredient. I didn't like it mashed, it was too soft, I would have preferred to eat it with the gravy and meat and beans, whole. But there was nothing else, that was the dinner, so I had some.

Father vanished behind the newspaper, and the headlines hit us in the face again. When he put it down he called out, 'Spread the bedding.' Mother spread his mattress on the floor at the back of the room, and gave him his blanket. He took his pillow and disappeared under the blanket completely. Mother spread her mattress next to his. They slept at the back of the room and our mattresses were spread at their feet at the front of the room.

It was soon after dinner that the bedding was spread out and we went to bed. Night had not yet fallen and it was still light outside. Shaba didn't like to use the oil lamp at night, so to save oil she would send us to bed before nightfall. Mother crept in with Vida, my baby sister, who slept next to her. I went to bed too, and my brother, who was five, slept beside me.

That night was a night like any other. I lay at my father's feet with only a small gap between us. If I looked up I could see him jumbled up under his blanket. I usually had no problem sleeping. I'd put my head down on the pillow and be fast asleep in a few minutes. But tonight I was either asleep, somewhere in a deep dream, or had just dozed off when a gruff murmur of voices woke me up. I opened my eyes under the blanket and listened hard.

'No, not like that, it hurts.' It was Mother's voice.

'Open your legs.'

'They are open.'

'A bit more, it won't go in.'

'You can't do it, it's coming out, let me sleep. I'm tired. The children are still awake.'

'It's OK, it's in now. Ohhhh . . .'

I tried desperately to put my head out and keep one eye open and see what was happening, but it was dark and I just saw my father's figure lumped on top of my mother, moving up and down. Fear haunted me in case they might see me awake; my body remained as still as a stick. A faint cry, and I heard my mother say, 'Have you finished?' as he rolled away from her and began to snore loudly.

I relaxed and unfroze my body, moved a hand and a leg, sighing with relief that they had not noticed I was awake and watching. All the movements and words came to my mind again and again, haunting me.

'Open your legs.'
'You can't do it.'
'Not like that, it hurts.'
'It's gone in OK.'

That night I stayed awake for a long time.

Two

We lived in the smallest dead-end alley – it had no name. There were three houses: one was ours; one was empty; and one was occupied by a woman and her three sons. We did not know much about them, and did not see them often, only when they came in and out of their house. But in Javady Alley – the one which joined ours – we had many neighbours. Haji was one of them; he had a fabric shop. His house was the nicest and the largest: he was the richest of our neighbours. He had been to Mecca as a good Muslim, that was why he was called 'Haji' (holy) by everyone, rather than by his own name. His wife was very fat, her neck and hands and ears were covered with gold jewellery, and even through the material of her black chador she made sure everybody could see her gestures flashing with gold. They had two daughters: one of them was Shahin, my friend. I would go to their house sometimes; it had a large courtyard and some beautiful plants. The thing I liked best was a large painting on the wall of their landing between the first and second floor. It showed distant green fields with a large tree and many birds flying in the sky. They had it repainted every year, and changed the scenery too. Each time I went to their house I stood before the painting and looked at it for a few seconds. I liked it very much.

Opposite Shahin's house was Farid and Farideh's house. Farideh was another friend. Their house was small like ours, and sometimes I played there with her. But I was cautious because my father said that Farideh's aunt wasn't a good woman. Farideh's father had left them, and she was earning bad money for the keep of her sister and her children; so we were not supposed to talk to them. I usually saw them sitting outside their house: two sisters talking. They were very fat, and I wondered how they moved around. When they sat in front of a large, round washing bowl, their heads bent as they washed clothes, they looked like rounded dough, kneading to and fro all the time. After they had done the washing they would pour the black soapy water down the lane. Javady Alley didn't have a gutter, but the next alley had one where all the filthy, lathery water went. This dirty water sometimes didn't reach the gutter and remained in the middle of the lane for a long time. This was a nuisance to us when we were playing games. When it did run into the gutter it left behind traces of dark grey scum and a horrible smell.

Mulla (a Muslim priest) was a respectable neighbour, and everybody said 'salam' to him when he appeared in the street. Women would stand up straight, covering their faces tighter and bending their heads humbly as they greeted him. He had two sons who usually played together. He was short and fat with a huge inflated belly like Haji's. Father said they had lots of money and ate as much chicken and beef as they liked, so that their bellies swelled up like balloons. Mulla lent money to the neighbours at a high rate of interest. We never saw his wife, except when their door was half open, when we would catch a quick glimpse inside their yard which was very clean. She was usually by the hoze, washing, but so well wrapped up in the black chador that we hardly saw her face. She never went out, and she spoke to nobody. We had heard that Mulla had just got another wife, aged thirteen, but we hadn't seen her. We tried hard to catch a glimpse of her, but it was impossible to see beyond that closed door.

Mulla and Haji were friends, and we often saw them chatting together in the street. When it was a holy time, Moharam or Ramadan, Mulla would read sermons in Haji's house and most of the neighbours would gather there to listen. If we saw Mulla coming when we were playing, we would quickly disperse and resume our game when he had gone by. He didn't like girls playing games, and each time he saw us he would tell us off, saying:

'Go home. It is not good for girls to play games. Go and help your mothers. Be good girls.'

He always gave us this advice.

7

Every afternoon, if it wasn't too hot, or too cold, women would sit around in the lane which was an extension of their small homes. They huddled in twos and threes, chatting while they knitted or cleaned rice and beans. Sometimes they cooked their annual jams, tomato puree and pickles together, over large wooden fires in the lane. This was done in summer when the fruits and vegetables were abundant and cheap. Sometimes there would be an argument between two women, and then the whole street would be full of shouting and excitement, peppered with loud insults.

The worst arguments usually happened between the havoos – or co-wives – who scolded, insulted, and sometimes hit each other in the middle of the lane. We had two co-wives like that further down our lane. We didn't know them well, except for their fights. It seemed that they were enemies who had to live together. Each woman would vanish as soon as she saw her husband appear at the end of the road.

There was an old man outside one house who always spent part of the day sitting on a low stool watching the children play and the street life go by. He had retired very late, he was half blind and half deaf, and very bony and small. His shoulder bones stuck out of his shirt like the sharp point of a small pencil. He was very kind, he liked children. He talked to us, asked us our names as he forgot them all the time, and smiled at us. But he was frightened whenever children played near his house. He was afraid that a ball or a stick would hurt him. He kept shouting out, 'Mind! Mind! Play further on! Be careful!' We called him 'Papa'.

My mother and grandmother didn't join in the daily chatting on the street. Shaba didn't because she only spoke Turkish, the language of the province of Iran where she had grown up, and didn't know Farsi: there wasn't anyone in the immediate neighbourhood who spoke Turkish. I didn't know why Mother didn't chat with the neighbours or have a friend in the street. This was despite the fact that she was the only woman in the street who could read or write, and usually wrote letters for other women, and read them too.

It was early afternoon; it was mild, and I was indoors. I heard noises and opened the front door. Outside I saw people moving furniture into the house next door that had been empty. I called out:

'Somebody's moving in next door.'

'Come in and shut the door, it's sleeping time,' my mother answered.

8

I lingered by the open door. After a while, when Mother was busy washing, I crept out. They had left the door open, and two men and a woman were moving in mattresses, blankets and boxes. I stood outside their door and watched them carrying things upstairs. There were some children running up and down too.

They were very excited to be in their new home. When everyone left to fetch more furniture I walked in through the front door. In the courtyard I could see their hoze, dried up and empty, but there were two large trees covered in leaves, and some flowers and fruit. Their grape vine was a very big one, growing up the wall, climbing over a trellis. On the adjacent wall was a dried up honeysuckle creeper. Near the hoze there was a tall wooden wardrobe, with a full-length mirror set in it. I stood in front of it and looked in the mirror. It was much taller than me. I was a tiny girl with short legs and small hands. I had on a short-sleeved summer dress made of soft cotton. It was printed all over with little flowers. I had dark skin, and two plaits of hair dangling on my shoulders. My eyebrows were bushy and black, covering my small forehead and hiding my large brown eyes. I smiled at the face: it was very plain. Suddenly another girl appeared next to me in the mirror; she was taller than I was with short, frizzy hair. She was browner than I was. Her large black eyes were clear and shining; I smiled at her in the mirror, and turned towards her:

'Is this yours?'

'Yes. Who are you?'

'My name is Homa. Is this your new house?'

'Yes. My name is Sara.'

'I live next door. This is a nice mirror.'

In the mirror was my face, my body: all that was me. I had seen myself – the person opposite was me, Homa. Anybody called 'me' meant that image in the mirror: how strange. That was a seven-year-old girl. I had had no idea of myself like that, as indeed I had had no idea of myself at all . . . This was the first time I had seen myself full length in a mirror. We didn't have such a tall mirror in our house.

Three

It was very early when I woke up. Father was eating his breakfast. He usually woke up early because he had to be at work for seven o'clock. Shaba rose before him for morning prayers at four. After these she wouldn't go to sleep as she had to make his breakfast and wake him up, and send him to work.

I sat up and opened my eyes. Shaba saw me: 'Go back to sleep, it's too early.' Father looked at me. 'Why are you up so early?' I put my head down, turned over and tried to go back to sleep. I couldn't. I watched my father take off his pyjamas and put on his overalls. Shaba was making his lunch-pack with her wrinkly fingers. He took a 50-rial note out of his pocket and held it out. Shaba handed him the lunch-pack and took the money.

'Are you coming home after work?' she asked.

'Yes,' he replied.

'Not staying out then?'

'No, not tonight,' he said.

He left the room and the front door closed behind him. Shaba bent to clear the sofreh. I got up.

'Can I have some breakfast? I can't go back to sleep.'

She poured the tea out and gave it to me. I sat cross-legged and rubbed my eyes, took the tea and put some sugar in it. It was odd. I was at the sofreh on my own, the room was still dark, the oil lamp burning on low. It seemed as if I was having breakfast in the middle of the night. Breaking small pieces of bread and putting them in my mouth, I took a sip of sweet tea each time to make the bread soft to swallow. Shaba was cleaning the samovar, everybody else was fast asleep.

'Have you finished?' Shaba asked me.

'Yes, I have.'

'Then thank God for giving us bread and sugar.'

'Why?'

'Don't question me. You mustn't question it. Because God is the provider . . . It could get worse, you know. As things are, we may

10

not have any bread to eat before long. I've seen those days. Don't be thankless: be a good girl.'

'All right. Thank you, God.' I clasped my hands together and looked at the ceiling in the way Shaba did.

'Can I wash the tea-plates?' I asked.

'No, I'll do it myself. Go and play.'

'Please,' I insisted.

'No, you'll break them . . . When you marry and have your own home, then you will do your own washing.'

I liked to wash the dishes and sweep the floor but they would never let me do it.

I went into the yard. It was both dark and light. The dawn was breaking, the sky was pinkish, growing redder and redder. I sat on the edge of the hoze. The water was still: there were no ripples, only calm and quiet. It was asleep too.

Where are the goldfish? Are they still asleep? I wondered. Where are they sleeping? At the bottom of the water? Perhaps there is a hidden tunnel and they have their bedroom down there. How do they sleep? Together? Or separate, like children? Perhaps they cuddle each other.

I wanted them to come up. I wanted to chase them. I put my fingers in the water and splashed them around. The splashes made small bubbles and they spread. The surface of the water curved and waved. The waves spread around, the bubbles grew bigger. They hit the wall of the hoze and dissolved. Red colour appeared from beneath the water. A goldfish came up and gulped the air. I had woken the fish up. Soon another appeared. Their scales shone under the dawn light. I chased them and they swam away. I hurried after them but they were afraid. They wouldn't let me get near enough to them. I could just touch them but they wouldn't come right into my hand. I wanted to hold them, just for a few seconds, but I couldn't. My palm must have looked like a prison to them. They were happier to swim away.

Mother came out with Vida on her arm.

'Homa, fetch the aftabeh and fill it with water.'

I ran to the toilet, got the water can and took it to my mother. She turned Vida around under her left arm and asked me to pour water on her bottom. There was some soft yellow shit stuck to it. With her right hand Mother cleaned the shit off, while I poured water. Pooh. It stank. I turned my nose away. The water, splattered with shit, ran

11

into the tiny gutter by the hoze into the drain. Vida's bottom was clean now; she was smiling.

'Can I hold her?' I asked Mother.

'Not here, come inside and watch her,' Mother said, 'while I prepare her nappies.'

Vida had little chubby hands and soft fat cheeks. I liked to play with her and kiss her cheeks. I held her but she was heavy, so I put her down and made noises to make her smile. Soon she was in clean nappies and in her bed – smiling all the time. Mother went back to the yard to wash the dirty nappies. Shaba had already put some water on the cooker to boil, so she took the hot water and poured it into the large copper washing bowl, added some cold water from the hoze and sat down to wash the nappies. I came up to her, holding Vida, and looked inside the washing bowl. She was separating the shit from the nappies, and bits of yellow were floating in the water. She had her arms up to her elbows in the washing bowl. There was so much shit there.

'How many times does Vida shit, Mummy?'

'I haven't counted yet,' she answered, not looking up.

'It seems a lot . . . hey, baby Vida . . . look at your master-pieces.' I tapped her on the back.

'You've forgotten yours.'

'Did I shit as much?' I asked doubtfully.

'What do you think?'

'Mm . . . so why do you have so many children?'

'I don't know,' she said, still separating the shit from the nappies.

I turned away. It made my stomach feel sick just looking at it.

Sometimes before dinner the courtyard got too hot to play in, so either I found a shady spot or went to the living room and played inside. I was resting after taking care of Vida; it was midday, before dinner-time. I was in the living room playing with my five stones. I had collected these five stones to match each other. Sitting cross-legged I would put them in front of me, then pick one up and throw it in the air. I'd repeat this until all the five stones were in my fist.

Then, reversing the process, holding the five stones in my fist I would put one down while I threw another in the air and caught it, and repeat this until all were on the ground. As my hand was small I couldn't usually hold them all at once, so I failed and would have to start the game again. I soon got bored. It was nice to play with the stones, but it was boring, especially doing it alone.

I went to the yard to see my grandmother. Shaba was cooking. The kitchen was just a cupboard under the stairs, too small for her to do the cooking inside it as it was also a storage place full of rubbish. So the paraffin cooker was inside the kitchen on the ground, and the pots and pans around it. She was frying aubergines in a frying pan. She was squatting by the cooker, half of her bent body inside the recess, half out in the yard.

'Can I help?' I asked.

'Yes, give me a plate.' I gave her a plate.

'But can I cook?'

'Not now, you will cook in your own home. Go and play.'

'I have played. It's too boring.'

'We're all going to eat soon.'

I still hung around her. The cooker was very small and had only one burner. Because it was on the floor, Shaba, who always did the cooking, had to bend over constantly.

'The aubergines need more oil,' I told Shaba.

'Yes, but we must use oil carefully, it's expensive.'

Still bending, she went to the other side of the yard to pick up pieces of aubergines which were drying there under the sun. When we had aubergines they would always be peeled first, then cut into long, flat pieces, salted and put in the sun to be part-dried before being fried.

'Shaba, why are you bending so much?'

'I'm an old woman.'

'Will I be bending when I am old?'

'No, you have a long time to go,' she told me comfortingly.

Shaba was frying the aubergines piece by piece in oil in the pan until they were nicely brown, and then laying them together on a plate. I saw her turn over each piece a few times to make sure it was properly fried and brown. She did this twenty or thirty times, over and over again. How boring: my eyes got tired watching her.

'Shaba, cooking is boring, isn't it?'

'You've got to eat.'

'Yes, it's nice eating it when it's just been cooked. Can't you make magic food?'

'Not yet, I've cooked everything except that.'

'Can I have a bit, just to try?'

'I'll give you a bit, but go away to the living room and eat it there quietly.'

She put a piece of well-browned aubergine on a plate and gave it to me. I went to the living room, got a piece of bread and ate it with enjoyment. I liked her giving me treats like this. She usually did it when there was nobody around. My mother was against it and said it was a bad habit and spoiled the children. 'Grannies always spoil children, giving them sweeties and bits of food before dinner-time,' she would protest. I wanted to be spoiled. Nobody else spoiled me except her.

Shaba shouted, 'Mina! Put down the sofreh, get the plates, lunch is ready.'

Mother appeared, spread the sofreh, put the plates down and Shaba brought in the aubergines in the pan, mixed with tomato.

'Homa, go and call Hamid, he's still playing in the street.'

Hamid was playing in some mud with his friends. He saw me and left his mud game and his friends and followed me home.

'Look at you, you're muddy all over.'

'Just building a house and garage for my car.'

He came towards me trustingly, showing me his little mud-covered plastic van.

'Mummy will kill you!'

By the hoze, he washed his hands and plastic van, and tried to clean his clothes. Mother screamed at him for making his only pair of trousers dirty. He was told he must stay in bed all afternoon until they could be washed and dried out in the sun.

After lunch, Shaba got ready to pray, standing up and bending down a few times, mumbling to herself very seriously.

'It's getting hot, you are not going out to play. Get ready for your afternoon nap,' Mother called to us.

I frowned and mumbled, 'Not so soon . . .'

'Yes.'

Soon after the dinner the beds were spread out. I didn't like going to bed but Mother was in a bad mood, fuming, so we had to. I lay on the bed under a soft cotton sheet. Even if I didn't sleep, there wasn't much to do: worse, it was getting hotter and hotter and we had to sleep longer. When there wasn't much to do, it was better to sleep. I closed my eyes and let sleep take me over.

When I awoke, Shaba was drinking tea, and asked me if I was thirsty and wanted some. I always preferred to drink water on hot summer days, but Shaba loved tea and drank it four or five times a day. I went to our clay pot and poured out a cup of cold water. It was like drinking from a mountain spring: it refreshed me and woke me up. I thought I could do something exciting: creep out and play with my new neighbour. I looked around to see if I could slip out unnoticed. Hamid always played out, but I couldn't because Mother needed me around the house. Sometimes I did creep out when she didn't notice, but I always got into trouble when I came back.

'Homa, watch Vida,' Mother called out to me.

Vida began to cry. Mother went to the yard to collect all the dried clothes from the line. All that she had washed in the morning had dried now under the afternoon sun. She folded a thick blanket into a neat square and put it down on the floor. The iron was in the yard and the charcoal blazed inside it. So Mother was going to iron and she needed me. I couldn't go out. I held Vida, shook her, tapped her on her square back and tried to make her smile and stop whining, but had no luck. I tickled her, hoping she would like it, but no, she carried on moaning.

'Keep her away from the iron.'

Mother brought the iron inside the room and put it on the side of the square blanket where the dried, crumpled clothes were heaped up.

I tried to keep Vida busy while Mother was ironing. She got down on her knees with a bowl of water, and the iron beside her. She opened my father's white shirt and sprinkled water all over it to dampen it, and then with special care she slowly pushed the charcoal iron over the back, the front and the sleeves. She ironed the collar a few times.

'Curse on your shirt, it won't stay flat . . . it's as stiff as a bone . . . it's that bloody starch . . .' she muttered quietly through her teeth.

She looked annoyed. I was annoyed too: I was tied to the baby and couldn't go out. Hamid was already out playing (why couldn't he take care of his baby sister?). The ironing lingered on, Mother grumbling, though I couldn't understand what she was saying.

Vida was whining. I nearly hit her. There was a tidy pile of folded ironed shirts and clothes beside her.

'Can you fetch me some more water?' Mother asked me, and gave me the bowl.

There were only some ties and hankies left to be ironed, so I was pleased. I left Vida on the floor, took the bowl, went into the yard, filled it with clean water, and brought it back. As I was entering the room I saw Vida crawling towards the iron. Mother was putting the ironed clothes away in the corner of the room. Before I could put the bowl down and run to her, Vida banged her forehead on the iron and screamed. I shouted 'Mummy!', the bowl falling to the floor. I caught her, Mother ran up and took her from me. Tears were falling down her round cheeks, her little hands were shaking in desperation. Mother walked up and down the room to soothe her.

'My sweet girl, oh my little baby, I'm sorry, don't cry, I should have watched you.'

There was a round, red, burnt patch over her left eye. I cleaned up the water that had spilled on the carpet, not knowing what to do.

Grandmother came in, frightened.

'This deadly hot iron looks like a torture instrument. I never ironed clothes in all my life, why do you? Curse on your fashions, my poor baby . . .'

'It's your son's clothes!'

'Throw the lot of them at him as they are, he should be thankful we work for him . . . Anyway, why are you doing it in the afternoon? Why can't you wait until the baby's in bed?'

'How can I?'

The red burn mark looked like fire itself; each time I looked at it my stomach turned over. Shaba suggested some herb medicine and prepared a hot drink. The poor baby had screamed herself to sleep. I cried for her.

When Mother started ironing the ties and hankies again she had a long, pain-stricken face. It seemed Vida's burn had marked her too. She sprinkled water on the ties and ironed them one by one, stretched out beside one another like long narrow ropes. With anger in her wrist, the veins on her hands standing out, she finished the square hankies too. She took the ties and hankies in her hand, weighing them thoughtfully, as if knotted together they would become like one thin rope, made ready for a hanging.

When Father came home that night he murmured, 'There's trouble,' and hid behind the newspaper. Nobody dared tell him about Vida's forehead. He didn't look at her either. He just read the headlines out loud, as he often did:

QUARREL BETWEEN PRESIDENT KASHANI AND DR MOSADEGH

PRESIDENT EISENHOWER'S WARNING TO IRAN: 'SETTLE YOUR DISPUTE WITH BRITAIN OR WE WILL STRANGLE YOUR ECONOMY.'

16

INDIAN GOVERNMENT ORDERS ARREST OF REVOLUTIONARY LABOUR PARTY

MAUMAU TERRORIST RAID ON ROYAL LODGE GIVEN TO THE QUEEN AS WEDDING PRESENT.

I was quiet and downcast all through the evening. In bed my eyes were open. I was afraid of fire and frightened of heat, although I didn't understand what had happened to Vida. I saw that the flesh above her left eye was swollen, reddened and crinkled. The burn looked like bread being baked in an open oven.

It's my fault that Vida's forehead is burnt, I told myself. I shouldn't have left her. I'll look after her all the time tomorrow. I'll be a good girl. I won't go out to play. I'll take good care of my poor sweet little sister.

Four

Vida was asleep, and when she awoke it was with a big sharp scream. I looked at her, the burn mark still worrying me. I waited around, helped Mother to wash, dress and feed her. Mother was extra gentle, careful, watching her forehead all the time, talking to her, calling her 'my sweet angel', holding her in her arms and rocking her. Mother was very kind and loving to her. Sometimes fear filled her face when she looked at the mark. Perhaps, like me, she felt guilty and responsible for it.

It was mid-morning. When Vida was asleep and Mother was sewing, I sneaked out. The tiny alley was half covered in sunlight: it was empty. At the turning of the alley the children appeared. Hamid was playing with some young boys at stone games, Sara was there too. I stood on the corner of the balcony, leaning against the brick wall, and watched them. Some big boys were playing alac do lac. They were divided into two groups, and, taking it in turns, one group started by hitting small sticks at the other group, using a larger stick as a bat. If the opposite group couldn't catch the sticks after a few tries, they were the losers and had to give the winners a

17

piggy-back. It was a very exciting game and I liked watching them stagger about carrying each other and falling off, rolling on the ground.

Sara was trying to play too. She hit at the stick but missed it as she couldn't throw it high enough. But she was good at catching. When she saw me, she threw her stick down and came running over.

'Salam, Homa. Do you want to play?'

'What shall we play?'

'Skipping?'

'Hmm . . .'

'I have a skipping rope at home. I'll go and get it.'

She disappeared into her house and soon came back with a washing line in her hands, skipping towards me.

'I'll do twenty, you count.'

She started off, one, two, three . . . circling on and on.

I called out, 'Twenty.'

'Now you try.'

She handed the rope to me.

'I'm not very good at it.'

'It doesn't matter, go on,' she told me.

I took the rope. I was afraid of trying, she made me nervous. I swung the rope up in the air but couldn't make it turn smoothly, so I stopped and started again. This time it was better, and the circles were perfect. We carried on skipping. Shahin joined us too. We each took our turn jumping up and down swinging the rope in circles over our head and under our feet on the same spot. We went on and on . . . It was fun, the three of us together and playing like this. Suddenly I heard Mother's angry voice:

'Where the hell are you, Homa? Come home.'

I threw the rope down, shouted, 'Bye, I must go,' and dashed in through the front door.

'Pour some water on my hands,' my mother snapped at me.

I hurried to the toilet, took the aftabeh and filled it with water from the hoze, and returned to her. She was holding Vida and wanted to wash her bottom. I poured the water over her, holding my face away so as not to see the shit. The smell hit my nose. I was annoyed at having to leave the game and face the yellow shit and its horrible smell.

'Give me the nappies and the pins,' Mother said.

Inside the room, I helped her to dress and put clean nappies on Vida. Mother nursed Vida's burnt forehead carefully afterwards.

'Can we have something to eat?' Mother asked Shaba.

'There isn't much to eat.'

'I'm hungry.'

'There is some money, take it. Go to the shops and buy some cheese. We can have bread and cheese.'

Mother gave Vida to me to look after and put on her chador, took the money and walked out of the sitting room with a long face, dragging her sandals behind her. She came back soon. Shaba had spread the sofreh and put all the bread in the middle in a small heap. As there wasn't enough of it she gave out rations. Mother had Vida on her lap. Vida had Mother's breast in her mouth, and was sucking it gently. She looked content, even with the burn mark still looking sore. Shaba put down the samovar and poured out the tea. Mother shared out the white cheese between us, bread and cheese with sweet tea, to soften it and make swallowing easier. She looked fed up and uncomfortable as she cut the bread with Vida still sucking her.

'Bread and cheese . . . is this a dinner? How can I breastfeed a baby and do the drudgery on such a poor diet? . . . Oh, I'm so tired of this.'

She sighed sadly, as if she had given up. Shaba, eating her share and looking content, said:

'Well, he will be paid today . . . it's not so bad, let's thank God . . . God willing, we will have a good dinner tomorrow.'

'If there is any money, that is, after tonight's spree, him and his drinking and women . . .'

'He says there is a lot of trouble in the factory, so he goes to meetings, not drinking.'

'Mmm . . . we shall see who will come at midnight, black with aragh.'

I ate the bread and cheese and sweet tea; it wasn't really so bad. Granny always said, 'Cheese is good for you.' But I would have liked it if we had had chips, preferably with eggs and tomatoes. Mmmm, that's tasty. That would be a rich lunch, I dreamed to myself. Perhaps we can have it tomorrow.

After lunch Shaba was up again praying. Covered all over and bending up and down, praying to God.

Mother was in such a bad mood, frowning all afternoon, that when she called 'Homa! to bed!' I slipped under the sheet at once and put my head on the pillow, looking out at the afternoon sun blazing in the yard. It was covering the walls, the surface of the yard, the pond. I don't want to sleep, I said to myself, I want to go out and play in the street. I missed so many games and activities, so much fun. I hated having to have an afternoon sleep just because the adults wanted to rest. It was so boring to sleep every afternoon, lie in the bed like someone paralysed and useless, and do nothing except dream.

Shaba warned us that we must be in as Father was coming home early that night. Every Thursday was pay day, and Friday the rest day, so there was something to look forward to. Father came in, throwing the newspaper on the floor. The headlines looked very big and black. He sat on the floor and mumbled the words out:

DEPUTIES RESIGN IN SUPPORT OF MOSADEGH. 28 SO FAR.

BRITAIN DROPS 1096 BOMBS ON MAUMAU IN 10 WEEKS

BRITISH LABOUR MP WEDGWOOD BENN RAISES DECISION OF KENYA SUPREME COURT TO SET ASIDE VERDICT ON JOMO KEN-YATTA

BRITAIN DROPS 25 TONS OF BOMBS ON SINGAPORE

Mother had prepared the hot water before Father arrived. Everything was ready, as Thursday night was a special night. He came in early, washed quickly but thoroughly, not only his feet, but also his neck and armpits. Mother poured out the clean, warm water to wash the dirt and soap off his body, and he was soon getting into his clean clothes. She handed him a pair of clean socks, into which he slipped his feet.

'Is my white shirt ironed?'

Mother quietly answered, 'It's hanging on the clothes rack.'

He took it and put it on, his arms sliding into the sleeves. Mother appeared with a long, narrow black tie hanging through her fingers. I was sitting cross-legged, leaning against the wall in a corner, watching. Shaba was also sitting and watching, turning her rosary around. Her eyes were looking up, uncertain. He took the black tie, put it round his neck, asked Mother for the mirror. She held a small, square mirror in front of him. He moved back a step.

'Hold it up . . . right, don't move.'

So she stood there upright, holding the mirror, its back to her face, while my father knotted his tie. It wasn't right. He unknotted it, and knotted it again, looking at himself seriously, sleek and content. After he had put on his coat Mother brushed his shoulders and he slipped into his nice, newly polished shoes and stood up.

'Homa, can you do up my laces, my little girl?'

I crawled forward on my knees and held the laces, wondering.

'No, I can't do them.'

'Why not?'

'I don't know how to,' I murmured.

'Why don't you learn it? Make yourself useful,' he said while he bent over to do it himself.

It didn't seem fun to do laces; it was boring.

Just before he left he took out a big packet of money from his pocket, and counted out a few notes to my mother.

'Pay the two weeks' rent arrears. I can't pay the whole of it this week, we didn't get our overtime. The bastards always get rheumatism in their hands when it comes to paying our wages.'

He gave a few notes to Shaba too, the housekeeping money, which she always took care of.

'Be careful with it,' he emphasised. 'Don't keep me any food, I'll be late.' He left the sitting room, and we heard the front door slam behind him.

'There he goes, off to spend the week's wages on vodka and women,' said Mother.

'Never mind that; there is nothing to eat. Go and buy some food,' Shaba told Mother.

'I need rest, I'm not hungry any more. He's gone off to enjoy himself, and we're stuck at home in this bloody hole all the time.'

'Thank God he is gone, the house is quieter and we are free from his anger and insults. Thank God, don't moan,' Shaba said, still fingering her rosary beads.

'Yes, thank God we are free from his anger and insults,' Mother repeated sarcastically. 'What a life, what a waste of my life. He has left his paper behind.'

She spread it on the floor.

'Perhaps he has gone to a meeting,' Shaba suggested.

'What kind of meeting? He doesn't tell us anyway.' Mother wanted to know, but didn't seem to care much.

She spread the paper wide open on the floor, looking all over it and reading the news out loud:

'DEMONSTRATIONS SUPPORTING MOSADEGH MARCH THROUGH THE TOWN! Look at the women there, they're demonstrating too, they're carrying red banners. One says – "No More Free Oil for Engelesia". Many are carrying Mosadegh's picture. Look! The army is marching with them too. One woman is sitting on a tank . . .

'Civil disorder in India over the increase in second-class fares continues. Resistance Committee of the tram passengers in Calcutta called for strike and refusal to pay the fare increase. Police attacked the passengers, they put up barricades and stoned the police . . . some attacked them with bombs.

'Oh God . . . all these people demonstrating . . . Um.'

She sighed, then turned back to the newspaper.

'Look at this picture. It says: "Kikuyu tribeswomen marching on a police station in Kenya. The British Army is dispersing them with batons. Women are thrown on the ground, their clothes are torn, and their bare bodies are hit with batons." '

Mother's eyes grew larger.

'How terrible! Why is the British Army hitting these women with batons?'

'Godless people will do anything,' Shaba remarked without even looking at it.

Mother was slowly shaking her head, sinking deep into thought.

Five

'What can I do?' I thought to myself. 'Is there anything interesting to do? . . . Nothing . . . nothing exciting to do. Everything is boring.'

I whispered to Shaba, 'Can you give me a penny?'

'What for?'

'I want to buy a lolly.'

'But you know your father doesn't give us much money, and none for such luxuries.'

'Please, just one penny.'

Shaba always wore long petticoats, with a long dress and waistcoat on top. She wore a scarf which covered her hair and neck, and also a chador even at home while working. Her clothing was the traditional costume of her village. She was the only woman I had seen who wore such clothes. She herself disapproved of city dress.

She had a purse hanging round her neck, inside her dress. As she pulled it out, I saw her chest was wrinkled like her face, and her breasts hung down.

'Why are your breasts hanging down?'

I spoke Turkish with her and she always tried to correct me and teach me it properly.

'I'm an old woman and I've fed five children, each for two years, with these breasts.'

She tapped them with her hand.

'They've been overmilked, that is why they are wrinkled like dried prunes.'

'Can I have a penny?'

She opened her purse and gave me a little one. I saw lots of pennies there and thought to myself how rich she was. The purse was closed and vanished inside her dress again.

I took the penny and left the house. As I turned from our alley into Javady Alley I saw Mulla appear on the road. His long black cloak was hanging from his shoulders, with a brown robe beneath, which looked meticulous, and on his head he wore a large turban. He was playing with his rosary and moving his lips. I turned back into our alley and hid until he passed by. I didn't like him and he scared me because he usually told us children off.

After he had gone I walked along the lane, keeping to the wall as I usually did when out alone. It felt safer. Also because the big boys were running around playing 'Bala Bolandi', which is a game where one boy runs after the others and they must get their feet off the ground or they will be caught. One boy was climbing up a wall, another one had safely reached the neighbour's step, while a third was hanging nervously from a tree branch over a wall.

At the end of Javady Alley I saw the sweet seller, sitting cross-legged by the wall with her candy tray resting on her lap. She was an old blind woman. Instead of eyes she had wrinkled skin over the sockets, and her eyelashes stuck out. Her face was as wrinkled as Shaba's, but she was much smaller and thinner. I sat down beside her and looked at the candies and lollies. I couldn't believe she was really blind, I felt that behind those little flaps of skin she was watching me all the time. The tray was full of sweets, covered with a glass lid so that no one could steal them from her.

'What would you like?' she asked, sensing that someone was there.

'I want a lolly.'

'What kind?'

'Oh . . . the cock one, the red coloured one.'

She lifted the glass lid and felt the candies and lollies with the tips of her fingers.

'Is it this one?'

'No.'

'This one?'

'Yes.'

She gave it to me. I took the lolly, which was in the shape of a rooster perched on a stick, and gave her the penny. She was sitting in her black chador and had her wooden walking stick on the ground beside her. She was our local sweet seller; she would come to this spot every day and all the local children bought their sweets from her. I didn't know where she lived, some people even said she lived nearby and didn't have to walk far, but I wondered what would happen to her if she fell over while she was carrying the tray of sweetmeats along.

I thought it must be very hard to walk when you can't see. I imagined I was blind and, closing my eyes, took a couple of steps forward, but I was afraid that someone might steal my lolly. I opened my eyes and set off home, licking the lolly, walking slowly along by the wall.

I was by the pond, looking at the goldfish and still licking my lolly. Hamid had a stick and was poking at the goldfish in the water.

'Don't, it will hurt the fish.'

He took no notice; he was licking a lolly too.

Sara put her head through the door and called to me to come out and play. Hamid wanted to come too. I looked around. No one had noticed her so I slipped out of the yard, with Hamid in tow.

'What game?' I asked.

'Let's skip. I've got a long rope and we can call Shahin and Farideh and we can do a game in pairs.'

I told Hamid to go and play with his own friends.

'You don't know how to skip anyway.'

'I don't want to play skipping with you, it's a girl's game.'

We set off to call for our mates. Sara asked for a lick of my lolly, so I passed it to her.

The rope was very long. Farideh and Shahin each held one end and stood in the middle of the alley. They were one pair, and Sara and I were another. It was our turn to skip first. They swung the rope into the air, forming a large arc, and back to the ground again. When the semicircle, moon-like, was in the air we jumped in and began to skip. The rope circle around us became wide and tight with their arm movements, and we skilfully cleared it each time it hit the ground. Then it was the other pair's turn to skip. Sara and I held the rope and swung it, our arms turning a full circle. I watched the rope, and thought of the fisherman's rope from the Caspian Sea, in the story that Shaba had told me, where women knitted nets, and fishermen threw them into the sea, to catch the fish that swam up and down and were entangled struggling in the net. Finally, Farideh and Shahin left us, and we packed up because we were bored too. Sara asked me to come to her house and play with her marbles. Their yard was smaller than ours, but they had trees there and we didn't.

The grape vine in Sara's courtyard had many bunches of unripe grapes which hung down over our heads. I liked them ripe, but my mother bought them like this and used them sour to add flavour to the cooking. The honeysuckle was in bloom. It covered a wall and snaked up over the top where it bent into our lane. The scent was beautiful and sweet. I wished we had green plants and flowers in our yard too. I picked some honeysuckle flowers and held them to my nose.

'Do you want to see our room?' Sara asked. 'Yes,' I answered with curiosity.

We went upstairs into a large room. Her father was sitting and smoking, the air was full of a strange smell. I was astonished at the size of the room, it was twice as large as those in our house.

'Do you sleep here?'

'Yes, we all sleep here.'

'How many of you?'

'Eight,' she replied.

There was a large picture of a beautiful woman, her hair and face made up, red lipstick on her lips, wearing a pretty skirt.

'She's beautiful, who is she?' I asked.

'She is my elder sister.'

'She's very good-looking, what a lovely photo.'

'Yes, she's a dancer in a cafe; there was a fight once and she was badly beaten up!'

'Oh . . . that's horrible! Why?'

'I don't know, it's the men there,' Sara said.

She came close and whispered in my ear.

'My father smokes opium.'

'Oh, so that's why the room stinks.'

'Yes. Mother gives me a tiny bit to eat when I'm ill and crying and can't sleep. She says it's good for putting children to sleep.'

I was puzzled.

25

'Really? I didn't know that.'

Sara seemed to know much more than me, she was freer and more active than I was. Her mother usually sat outside in the street chatting with other women, so she didn't mind Sara playing there.

But my mother didn't like it, and she didn't have time to watch me as she was so busy at home doing all the housework and looking after the baby. When I went inside after playing out she was too tired to tell me off or punish me, she would just find me something to do.

Sara had three elder brothers, one a grown man, and one two years, the other four years, older than her. She also had a younger sister who was four. We sat down by the pond under the grape vine and played five-stones together. First she threw, then I did. We were sitting by the wall which divided our two houses, quietly out of the way of adult eyes. I could hear movements in our house . . . somebody was pumping the water, sandals flopping around. Suddenly I heard Vida's cries, getting louder and louder. Mother called out my name. Afraid that I might be beaten for playing outside, I gave Sara the marbles and dashed out. As I came into the yard my mother yelled at me:

'Where the hell have you been? Playing in the street again! Take your sister, she's crying her eyes out. I've got to wash these sheets and pillow cases.'

She had a huge pile of white sheets beside her as she knelt by the large washing bowl, up to her arms in water. I went to Vida and picked her up. She stopped crying.

'Yes, yes, come on now, smile, smile . . .'

After a while she smiled at me. I looked at her forehead, the burn mark was still very big but looked better. I wasn't sure whether I could touch it, so I didn't.

'Let's walk. You can try now, you're a big girl.'

I held her arms and pushed her forward. She took a step forward and fell on to her bottom, whining a little.

'Try again now, come on, walk.'

I pulled her up and tried to make her walk again. This time it was better: she took two or three steps, and I let go of her hands to see if she could do it without my help. She took half a step, but saw her hands unsupported and fell again, this time screaming. As soon as I lifted her up I heard my mother cry:

'What are you doing to her?'

I took her in my arms and paced the yard up and down to try and

26

quieten her. I was angry.

'Useless girl. You can't walk. You don't even try. Useless baby. Good-for-nothing. Why don't you learn?'

I brought her over to where my mother was washing. The sun was hot, beads of sweat were running down her forehead and into the water. She was wringing the huge white sheets, which were only slowly losing their dirt. It was nearly lunch-time, but she still had a big pile to wash. I was hungry.

'Mum, I'm hungry.'

'You'll have to wait. I must finish these before lunch so they can dry in the afternoon sun, and I can iron them for tonight.'

'But it will take you ages to get them clean,' I complained.

'Well . . . '

Mother just mumbled. Inside the washing bowl the water was grey, turning to black with some soap bubbles.

The afternoon sun was really hot. There was no shady corner in the yard, the sunlight spread to every corner of the house: yellow, brazen, and hard. The goldfish had disappeared to the bottom of the pool in search of some cool, soothing shade. The hot afternoons were calmer and quieter than usual. It was always the case when the weather was hotter: the streets and markets were quieter, and people slept much longer than usual. The white sheets on the washing line across the yard were baking in the sun, steam rose from them, as if the sun was working extra hard to dry them. The sheets divided the yard up into several compartments, each with a whitewashed cotton wall. A maze, alleys of white cotton, lines and walls that divided the sun too, shadows of the sheets on the ground. The sound of insects and flies buzzing. Summer heat meant the migration of flies into our house. I saw the sheets dividing the sun, the yard and the pond; white squares that covered us all; flies buzzing in and out of the maze.

The sheets were bone dry when the afternoon sleep had run its course, and the sun was retreating into its lost home.

The iron was ready, the blanket on the floor, and I was told I must not leave Vida for a second. Mother was sitting cross-legged on the floor, the sheets scattered before her in a large square.

She had to bend over and stretch as far as she could reach. I held Vida and watched the process, desperately hoping it would finish soon. Mother was mumbling under her breath, all I could catch was:

'It's hell, this life of mine, perfect hell.'

I didn't mind when she talked to herself alone, but I was embarrassed when she did it in front of other people.

Mother placed the sheets on top of the bedding pile. They were folded up with the pillow cases. They looked white, clean and tidy, and very welcoming. She would put them on the beds at night after she had spread the mattresses. I liked looking at and feeling the clean sheets: they smelled of fresh, cool cotton; they meant health and caring.

I saw Mother sitting down resting, either exhausted and numb, or in deep thought. When she rested (or had a chance to) she often went blank like that, as if she didn't see anything around her. Her eyes were fixed and glazed-looking.

I had to say 'Mum, Mum,' four times, and shout; then she would say, 'Yes? Are you calling me?'

Father came in frowning, more angry than usual, the newspaper rolled up under his arm.

'I must go out soon, get the dinner ready,' he shouted to my mother. Shaba sensed that things were not right and started to move fast.

'What's wrong?' Shaba whispered.

'There is trouble, you stay at home, you don't know what's happening outside.'

'So what? Anyone would think the world was coming to an end the way you're giving out orders.'

He just grunted in reply.

'Where are you going, anyway?' Mother asked softly.

'Just to a meeting in Ali's house.'

Ali was his close friend.

The preparation of the dinner in the yard was swift. Father was putting on his clean shirt and looking in the handmirror when he gazed at Mother for a second and then yelled:

'Why have you got that red blouse on?'

'I haven't got anything clean,' Mother quietly answered.

'Take it off, that brazen whore blouse.'

'I haven't got anything else to wear, I washed all my clothes today.'

Silence followed for a few seconds.

'Take it off, I said. Red is the colour of whores. You know I hate it.'

He was mad, his eyes red with anger.

28

'You don't buy my clothes, why should you . . .'

She was going to say something more, her mouth open, but Father moved towards her in a rage, half of his shirt buttons undone, his face deeply creased. He stretched his arm out, it looked so long, raised it, and threw it like a long sword at her face and hit her sharply. Her mouth was left open in shock and the unspoken words were lost in the sound and pain of the attack. He put on his clothes fast while Shaba protested:

'Some strong man you are . . . aren't you? You can beat up a woman. God forgive you.'

'Fuck your God. I fuck your God.'

As he swore he had his hand on his prick, making the gesture. He left without eating his dinner. We were all in a state of shock, a dull haze of violence.

'He is going to a meeting,' Mother sarcastically repeated. 'Shit on your meeting. Shit on your mates. Shit on the paper you read every day.'

'See how much you have learned! You shouldn't wear red, not in front of him, anyway. Don't bother yourself, he's in such a temper because of his hard work in the factory, and his nonsensical politics are emptying his brain.'

Shaba tried to comfort Mother.

'Yes, those stupid irrelevant politics, preaching, preaching like the mulla in a pulpit to others. Do this, do that, do as I tell you, bossing everybody around. Shit on your communism, shit on your politics. And *you* carry a red flag!'

Mother was holding her slapped cheek with her hand. She was bitter, desperately bitter. Mother spat, as if spitting on his face, on his confidence, on his belief. Shaba didn't try to utter another word of either protest or comfort. She looked dull, drunk, in a stupor, not knowing what to say or do.

Six

Sara was my friend now and we played together quite a lot. Playing with her was fun and very enjoyable. It was good to have a close friend, somebody to play with, to talk to and make games and run around with. It was very exciting to play with Sara. She usually came to call for me and then I would wait for a suitable moment when I was not needed to go out. We played many games together, some at home and some in our lane.

One day Sara and I went out to play. The wide lane was crowded with big boys. They took up a large area, so we couldn't play there. It was like this always in summer holidays. They invaded all the space in the street. They were having a good time playing the belt game, which had ended with all ten of them in a large circle, the five winners beating the five losers with their belts and all of them moving around, laughing, joking noisily.

So we came back to our lane and drew large hopscotch squares and Sara held the stone and started. She hopped from the first square to the end and then hopped back down. She was fast and energetic and was winning. I was slow and careful and had shorter legs, so I couldn't hop as fast. She soon owned a few squares, or 'houses', and I had difficulty hopping and avoiding them. When she threw the stone and it landed on my house's line I told her that was wrong and it was my turn, but she didn't listen to me and went on playing. I got very annoyed and took the stone from her but she pushed me back and forced it out of my hand. I told her that she was wrong and a bully and I wouldn't speak to her any more. I left her and went home miserably.

Usually after a quarrel with my playmates I would go home to sulk and play on my own. I went to my corner which was between the blanket and bedding bundles and the wall, a dark corner where I could hide and be by myself. Everybody was busy doing the housework. I took my string and sat in that quiet corner to think, and play cat's cradle. I would weave the string between my fingers and, with the fingers of the other hand, catch each loop and shorten it, until I had a maze of different shapes caught between my fingers, nice shapes, patterns all tangled up in my ten fingers. I did it and undid it, until I got bored with it. I was still annoyed with Sara.

Sara was a strong and active girl. It was a pity that she was bossy. I didn't like her stubbornness. She failed, she made mistakes, but she wouldn't accept it. She wouldn't accept my words and pushed me around when she didn't like what I said. When she became rough and struck me, I left her and told her that I wouldn't play with her any more, nor speak with her until the 'Days of Justice'.

My corner was dark and warm, small and cosy, only big enough for me to sit down cross-legged and be hidden from the eyes of adults, who, when they saw me, either ordered me to do a chore or blamed me for not doing any. So I preferred to play with string rather than marbles, because they were noisy. I went on knotting and unknotting the string, on and on till I heard my mother call my name.

I came out of my corner. She wanted me to help her spread the sofreh. It was dinner-time and Shaba was getting the samovar ready, making the tea. Mother was bringing in the tea plates, talking to herself.

'What is there to eat?' I asked.

'Well . . . today's lunch is a poor one, sweet tea and bread,' Shaba said quietly.

We sat around the sofreh, Mother, Hamid and me. She poured out the tea and gave a cup to everybody. The tea was pale pink in the glass cups, with steam coming out of it.

'We have sweet tea and bread for breakfast, sweet tea and bread for lunch, sweet tea and bread for supper . . . what a fine diet. How can we survive on such food?' Mother quietly but painfully protested.

All of us were sitting and eating but we were gloomy.

'Don't be thankless to God, it is not so bad . . . don't infuriate him, he can even take this bread away. He could be less generous, you know,' Shaba said patiently.

'Thank God? Really, can it get any worse?' Mother protested loudly and threw away the piece of bread in her hand. The bread landed in the middle of the sofreh where there were many pieces of small, dried, stale bread collected in a little heap. They were a few days' rejected bread that Shaba did not throw away in case we needed it. When there was a shortage of fresh bread she would usually soak the stale pieces in her sweet tea and eat them with a spoon. She would say to us:

'Well . . . I have no teeth, it is good for me to soak my bread.'

She told me that we shouldn't reject any piece of bread or waste it, it took such hard work, cost the farmers so much sweat and blood to produce the grain. We shouldn't throw it away, they would be hurt and then complain to God that we had rejected this bread or that rice, and then God would get angry with us and punish us. Mother called all that nonsense.

'Shaba is an old woman and doesn't know what she is talking about . . .'

31

She still went on and complained under her breath . . .

'I have never had a proper meal since I left my father's house.'

Shaba liked God very much, and whenever we had a poor dinner, which was quite often, she said we must pray to God and thank him and ask him to make it better for us. She herself prayed three times a day. In the morning she woke up very early, at dawn: if she overslept and the sun was out she had to do a late prayer, which wasn't as good. She fasted during Ramadan, regularly. She also had a long rosary in her hand that she continuously counted, while reciting parts of the Koran in praise of Mohamad and Ali. Shaba liked heaven, didn't want to go to hell. She wanted to be in heaven near her Mohamad and Ali, that's why she praised their greatness all the time. Mother said Shaba didn't have anything better to do.

Shaba was putting down our mattress for the afternoon sleep.

'I can't sleep, I'm still hungry,' I told her.

'If you sleep you forget your hunger.'

'But I'm not sleepy, I'm hungry. I can't sleep when I'm hungry. I'm thinking about food all the time.'

'I'll tell you a story, a nice long story to get you to sleep.'

'Oh, what kind of a story? Is it a fairy tale? I like fairy tales.'

'It isn't a fairy tale, it's a true story, it's my story.'

'Oh, lovely, I like a true, real fairy tale.'

I got into bed quickly and waited for her to begin. She sat down by my bed, gazed into the air thinking hard, tracing her past.

'When I was a young woman I lived in this village in Azerbaidzhan. My husband died young. I had six children. He left us for heaven and we were without a breadwinner. My two elder daughters were married and had their children and husbands and lived separately. I was left with four children and I didn't know how to earn their bread. My eldest son was sixteen then, and he managed to get himself a job as a farm hand with one of our relations in the village. So now I had three children, a son of thirteen, a younger boy of seven and a girl of five, to support. I was very poor, hadn't any money and he hadn't left us anything when he died. I took the kids with me and went from house to house in our village to ask if they wanted a home help, a farm hand or a washer woman. But I couldn't get any job, everybody in our village was poor and they all did their own work themselves. They couldn't pay wages to anybody. Usually families worked for each other, and weren't paid at all except for food and tea while working.

'One day a man from the village brought news to us which was very interesting.' Shaba paused for breath and rolled the rosary in her hand. I was quiet. I didn't want to say anything in case she forgot to tell me the rest of the tale.

'The news was that the new government in the Soviet Union was trying to build the country and get rid of the poverty and disease and needed many workers to help them. They were asking for workers. It was a people's government and it was promising jobs to everybody. The people in the part of Azerbaidzhan which is in the Soviet Union spoke Turkish, therefore they were our people too. Some men in the village became happy and decided to go. Others wanted to go and needed a job, but said that they weren't sure about living in a foreign country, and didn't want to leave their families behind, so they preferred to stay in the village with no job and no money. I was glad to hear this news. I could take my children there and get a job to earn my living. I said I would go. Some men laughed, but I didn't take any notice of their jokes and contemptuous remarks . . . "A woman travelling across the country to a foreign land . . . with three children . . . she must be soft in the head," they said, or "That kind of woman looks for trouble." So I got ready and packed our things and met the men from the village who were going, and set off with the group. I was the only woman, except for my daughter, among those men.

'It was a long journey, very very long and troublesome. First we travelled on donkeys, then coaches, changing coaches, getting a boat to the Soviet Union and then another long coach trip to Bakú, the city where we settled. It was easy when we got there, we were given somewhere to live, then I got a job and sent the children to school and to vocational training centres. That was a hard period, but it was a constructive period of my life. The children were educated, I got married again and my young daughter got married a few years after. That picture on the mantelpiece is her with her husband and children. They still live there . . .' Shaba paused; tears came to her eyes, which she wiped with the corner of her scarf.

'Now you sleep and I'll tell the rest of my story some other time.'

'Oh please, Shaba, I can't wait. At least tell me the end of the story.'

'Well . . . it ended like this. Just before the Second World War the Shah of Iran, the father of this Shah, asked the Russian Government to send the Iranian citizens home. Because of the war, the Shah was going to close the border. They issued notices all over Bakú and other places and told the Iranians that if they wanted to go back to Iran they should do so, but if they didn't they could stay as Russian citizens and could not return to Iran ever again. I was pining for my country, for our land. Nowhere is like home, you know: whatever the hardship at home, you feel safe there. So I took your father, and your uncle Amo Salim, and started the journey back. My daughter couldn't come because her husband was Russian.'

'What happened to your husband? Did you have any children from him?'

'No I didn't, that is another long story. I'll tell it to you another time, I'm tired now. Go to sleep because I want to sleep too.'

She looked sad, the tears still sparkled in her eyes but didn't drop down. Perhaps she was tired of remembering a hard life. Now I wasn't sleepy at all.

I liked Shaba. She was so kind, so nice – so much nicer than Mother. I enjoyed listening to her story: nobody usually told us any stories or had the time to talk to us. I was so interested in it that I only swallowed saliva when she paused. I didn't blink, didn't even move a hand or a leg: I was listening to her from head to toe.

What an interesting life story she has had, I thought, travelled so much by boat, on a donkey, by coach, been to different places, done different things. I imagined her life story, closed my eyes and in my mind I tried to picture all that she had told me. I'd like to travel too, on a donkey, in a boat.

When Father came in he knew that there was no money in the house and no food either. He gave money to my mother and said that he had had to borrow some from a friend.

'Get some potatoes and bread,' he said.

'We have no cooking oil or paraffin for the cooker,' Shaba said.

Mother put on her chador and took the money note from Father's hand and the paraffin jar from the kitchen and walked off. Father was behind the newspaper, only the top of his head showing.

There was a small knock on the door and Afagh put her head through the door.

'Mr Eby, I would like to talk to you, could you come up please?'

Father looked up, he was so surprised. He slid the newspaper down and nodded his head in agreement.

'I'll be with you soon.'

Afagh didn't come in, but closed the door and went to her room waiting.

Father was annoyed. 'She's worried about the few weeks' rent arrears.' He said it disapprovingly.

'She is a widower and has no breadwinner, and has to pay for her son's education herself,' Shaba said, to placate him.

'She has property, she has orchards, she was left a great inheritance. What more does she want? . . . she is just a mean woman, living on unearned money.' He said it while moving uneasily, playing with his moustache. He was reluctant to go up. He knew what he was going to hear and didn't like it at all.

Afagh was a literate middle-class woman. She was small, slim, with sharp eyes and a bony face. She was very polite, well-mannered and spoke without swearing. Mother said that she was a clever woman but Shaba said that she liked money more than anything else, that she was mean and hard, not a kind woman.

'How are you? How is work?'

'All right . . . fine.'

'As you know, Mr Eby, Shapor is only a student. I have to support him. You owe us a few weeks' rent. You must have been paid.'

'No, I am very short of money. There isn't much work and our wages are not paid on time . . . I thought Shapor was earning good money in the military school and that he is not dependent on you.'

'No, that's not right. He only gets some pocket money for his personal expenses, peanuts really.'

'Oh . . . really . . . Um . . .'

'You work hard and you do overtime, you shouldn't be short of money. The rent is really cheap, you know, and that's because we are relations. It would be much higher anywhere else.'

'Well . . . um . . . of course . . . I don't know . . .'

'You must think about my position too, I am my own breadwinner.'

'How is the harvest this year? Have you had news from home? Has any money come through yet? I hope there is no bad news there.'

'Well . . . no, not much really, there is news but not good news. There are a few serious problems, two labourers have suddenly been taken ill, some kind of pest is damaging the fruit and I'm planning to go and sort things out.'

'I'm sorry for that, yes . . . it is a problem. . . . well . . .'

'What's happening in your factory. You aren't mixed up with any of these troublemakers, I hope?'

'We also have problems, we're asking for decent wages, safer conditions at work and sick pay. We're going slow, that's why our overtime isn't paid yet.'

'That's a lot to ask . . . how can you expect all that if you don't work hard to prove you are good workers and observe the factory regulations!'

'Oh . . . well, we are asking for better work conditions . . . we are going slow because we can't get them any other way.'

'Mr Eby, I am like your mother, I have your welfare at heart, listen to me, don't get mixed up with the troublemakers. The reds are the godless, they will ruin us. Be a good worker, you are young and strong, this country needs good workers like you. You are a family man, you earn good money, don't ruin your chances, work hard for your country, take care of your family.'

'Look, I will try to pay you as soon as I get my next wages. I hope soon. I must go down now, I haven't eaten yet, I'm hungry.'

'I hope so, Mr Eby, don't forget it, see you soon then.'

He came in and slammed the door behind him.

'That stupid woman . . . God, she is so empty-headed, telling me to work, to be a good worker and work hard.'

Shaba jumped.

'What's wrong? The door nearly fell off.'

'I don't give a damn, let it fall off, let the whole house fall down, why should I care, Mina doesn't. It is all her fault, my own wife's fault that now we are tenants. We could have bought this house four years ago when it was very cheap. She wouldn't have it, she didn't co-operate, didn't want to put down any of her money. I begged her. It was a good opportunity: with both of our money we could have owned this house now. She said no, I won't give you my money, I won't trust you. I said it would be in our name, both our names, or if you don't believe me, we will make it in the children's names. But still she wouldn't do it. I even gave her all the redundancy money, put it in her hand, she wouldn't bend. She's a bitch, a careless bitch. She never cared for us to have a house, for her own family. Stubborn woman, deaf, bloody inconsiderate, so Afagh took the opportunity, she bought it and I am now paying my wages to her as rent. My money went, vanished, disappeared completely. But she invested her money with a miser and is getting the interest every month, God knows what she spends it on. I don't know, perhaps it's all piling up in the bank, keeping for her future, while I tear my guts out to feed her and the children, thankless slut.'

He was bitter and angry, feeling betrayed by her and humiliated by Afagh. Shaba, who was listening to him, tried to calm him down.

'Her money is your money too, she doesn't have much now – you know she spends her money here, on the house, and the kids.'

'I don't believe that. She must be piling it up somewhere for her future, not for us.'

'She spends it when you don't have money, she does buy food, clothes for the kids – she has just bought a school uniform for Homa, and a pair of shoes for Hamid. She spends it in your house, man. Don't worry.'

'Hey . . .' sneering, 'so what . . . that's really soft-headed, spending money on uniforms! A girl's education is more important than owning a house, a roof over your head! No wonder they say a woman's brain is in the soles of her feet. I know she is against my will, against my choice. She is an indecent slut, the bitch . . . against me.'

Mother walked in, hot bread in one hand, the paraffin container in the other, holding her chador with her teeth, as if chewing it. She must have heard the last few words, the insults to her, but she turned her eyes away as if she didn't care. She had heard it too many times. She looked listless and irritated. Perhaps she had had to queue for a long time. She looked too tired to get angry. She put the bread down, took off her chador, and sat down to get her breath back.

Seven

'What are you eating?' Sara came out with a sandwich in her hand every morning. She was munching away, not completely woken up. This was her breakfast and she ate it in the alley.

'It is ghosht kobideh [mashed abgosht], left over from last night.'

'Is that what you have for breakfast?'

'Yes . . . it's nice.'

'I don't like ghosht kobideh.'

'I like it. We eat it every night. It's good for you.'

She went on munching and waking up more and more. She was

nearly finished when she noticed a boy down the lane, riding a bike.

'Oh, look, Ali has got a bike, let's go and see! Oh . . . he's trying to ride it. That's great, come on.'

Before I knew where I was she was running down the road and I was following her. When we got to Ali, a big boy ten or eleven years old, he was riding the bike round and round in a circle.

'Let's ask him for a ride,' Sara said very excitedly.

'No, I can't, I don't know what to do with a bike,' I said fearfully.

'You ride it.'

'I don't know about riding a bike, I've never tried it before.'

'Well, neither have I, but we can try.'

'But I'm afraid . . .'

She went ahead and borrowed it.

'I'm afraid of trying, I'll fall down, I don't like falling down.'

'You are a whiney little girl, aren't you?'

Sara was already on the bike. It was too big for her but she was struggling to fit it. The handlebars were wide and she had difficulty holding the machine up. Hamid was running after a big tyre with a stick, pushing it down the middle of the lane and running after it. Sara managed to pedal once or twice but she soon fell down and the bike collapsed over her. She stood up, rubbed her grazed knee and tried again. I stood on the safe corner under the shade of the balcony and watched her try again and again till she managed to cycle. She was pleased and smiling. I was excited and would have liked to ride it now but I didn't know how to ask. I was afraid if I fell down the others would laugh at me. I didn't want to be laughed at.

Sara shouted at me, 'You must try it, it's such fun!'

But I stayed under the shade of the balcony and watched her.

Sara and I went to her house to play under the shadow of the grape trellis. It was a large grape vine full of the green leaves with which Shaba made delicious dolmas. The grape bunches were hanging down, like beautiful earrings. They weren't all red yet, still pinkish, but the sun was so hot that Sara's mother said they would be ripe and ready to eat very soon. The trellis covered the whole yard; underneath it was cool and shadowy. It looked safe and secure. I wondered who had built it and why the grape vine needed the trellis to lean on.

We sat by the hoze and Sara said that she wanted to show me something. She went to fetch it, and came back with a box in her hand.

'What is it?' I asked her.

38

'Come closer and look inside . . .'

'Oh, what kind of insect is it?'

'They're silk worms, aren't they beautiful? They're my brother Hosein's pets. He got them yesterday.'

'Oh. How strange, what does he do with them? How does he look after them?'

'He likes them, he gives them mulberry leaves to eat, but he's mean and doesn't let me play with them.'

I looked inside the box. It was very dirty.

'He hasn't cleaned it!'

'No, he just likes to play with them and he wants me to clean the box for him, but I tell him to get lost.'

'They're crawling around. What's that yellow string coming out of them?'

'He says they shit this yellow string, which is silk, and they wrap it around themselves all over until each is covered in its cocoon, and then they turn into butterflies and try to tear the cocoon open and fly away . . .'

'Really? Just imagine it, they're magnificent.'

I had never met a child who had a butterfly as a pet.

Shaba was squatting by the cooker in the cupboard kitchen and frying the potatoes. We were going to have chips for dinner. I liked chips. What a luxury, yummy, yummy, chips in my tummy, great.

'Homa,' Mother called me, 'give me the dustpan.'

I took the dustpan to her. She was sweeping the sitting room. The door was wide open and I could see her bending over, brushing the carpet thoroughly. She had her chador wrapped round her neck, covering her hair and most of her face, but not her nose. The dust was rising up and covering the air and herself. The dust hit my face and found its way down my throat. It was uncomfortable, so I gave her the dustpan quickly and left the room. I didn't like the dust. When I breathed it in it made me cough. It always happened when Mother was sweeping the room or the yard, which got even more dusty. I don't know why it didn't bother Mother, she still swept on even when she was choked with the dust and the dirt, and coughing in fits. She went on and on sweeping for a long time when she could have just given it a quick brush and finished it quickly. I didn't like sweeping, it was a nuisance. Mother shouldn't have to do it.

The newspaper in Father's hand was folded and crumpled up small. He looked angry. He was mumbling under his breath.

'Fucking hell . . . damn it.'

'What's wrong, why can't you come home with a happier face?' Shaba asked him. The early part of the evening was the only time for the family gathering. We were all in the living room, each doing something: Mother serving Father, Shaba looking after everybody, Father reading the paper and discussing the news with himself, and us children sitting around and doing errands when we were called to do so. Although we were all together we were hardly together really, communicating with each other. Conversation between us was very short and mainly about things we had to do or hadn't done. Arguments, disagreements and swear words were the main part of the daily conversation in our house. In between there were cold silences.

So our house could be very quiet and monotonous at family gathering time. It could be so boring that I would either fall asleep where I was, or choose to go to bed and sleep.

I was too afraid of my father to break the silence: I was afraid of being told to shut up if I said something, or of saying something stupid that made them laugh at me. But sometimes I did try quietly to ask a question or make a comment, taking the risk and hoping that I wouldn't be punished.

Tonight the news items were read in silence, hints of anger and disappointment coming out only through half swallowed words. Whatever there was in the paper deeply involved my father.

'Mosadegh is wrong, he is leading himself to destruction, damn it,' I heard.

He muttered again from behind the paper: 'He has to pull himself together.'

'Who is Mosadegh?' I asked timidly.

He went on reading without answering me. I waited a little bit, and as I wasn't shouted at, plucked up some courage and asked again. He lifted his head from behind the paper and looked at me. I put my head down, feeling shy. He continued reading the paper again. But soon he paused, looked at me again. I must have asked a very odd or difficult question . . .

'Mosadegh is our Prime Minister.'

He was still looking at me with his small blue eyes, perhaps feeling sorry that he had answered. But what he had said created another question in my head. I'd better ask it while he is there.

'What is a Prime Minister? What does this man do? Why does he make you so angry?'

It all came out fast before I knew where I was. He put the paper down, gave me half a smile which I found greatly encouraging, and began.

'Mosadegh is our Prime Minister. It means he is a man we have voted for to be the head of the Government. His job is to make decisions about how to run the country, about building factories, hospitals, schools. He is a very important man. Mosadegh is a popular Prime Minister, people like him. He's changing a lot of things, and that is good for us, good for people. I get angry with him sometimes because he also makes wrong decisions and it will be bad for him and for us.'

The words came too fast for me to understand everything that he was telling me, but I thought I could repeat them in my head and therefore remember. Perhaps I could understand them later. Shaba butted in:

'Don't fill her head with the same nonsense that your head is filled up with. Politics doesn't make bread, much less so if you are always talking about it. Homa, come and help me get the dinner plates ready. Don't listen to him. If there was common sense in his head he would work hard to look after his family. Put the sofreh down properly without any creases.'

'All right, Shaba.'

I didn't know why she was so mad. She never liked newspapers and disagreed with Father's talk about the news. She would always say, 'It is rubbish, nothing to do with us, it won't make bread for us. This is the most important thing, bread, we need bread, food first, everything else should come after.' That is why she didn't like Father to talk about news, especially when we didn't have food to eat. She said that he was wasting money on buying the bloody paper when we could do with the money for something more useful, like medicine for her eyes. I put down the sofreh and helped to serve the dinner, which was stewed red beans with potato. I was very annoyed that Shaba didn't let our conversation go on: perhaps I could have asked more questions and found out more.

We'd had our dinner, Shaba was cleaning the sofreh, Mother was getting ready to do the washing up by the hoze. There was a knock on the door. I ran and opened it. It was my Amo Salim, Father's elder brother. I said 'salam', and asked him to come in. Father stood up and welcomed him; he was smiling, happy to see him.

41

They greeted each other, as usual with jokes and laughter.

My father patted Amo's big belly and said, 'How is this belly? Getting bigger all right.'

My Amo patted Father's bald head and said, 'Your hair is growing, soon you will need to buy a comb.'

They came in and sat down to chat.

'How is my young bride?' Amo asked Shaba in thick heavy Turkish.

Shaba was pleased to see him.

'I'm dying, stop teasing me, how are you? How are your wife and the children?'

'They're all right and well, and the children are growing fast and eating more, which is a problem. They're in good shape, healthy, no ailments, that's the most important thing. Thank God for that.'

Amo usually came to visit us alone – he seldom brought his wife or children. This was bad because his daughter was my age and I liked playing with her and my cousin, who was older than me. It seemed men liked to go out alone or with other men, not with their wives and children. We only saw them together once a year during the New Year celebrations, at the beginning of Farvardin, when the Persian spring begins.

Amo Salim looked at Mother with special reverence and asked her, in Persian:

'How is Mina, our dear bride?'

'Thank you very much, I'm fine. How is Simin, the children?'

'Well, all well, so far so good. They send their greetings.'

Mother cheered up. I think she liked Amo because of his cheerfulness, the respect he had for her, and the attention he paid her.

'Does Eby look after you properly? He hasn't misbehaved, has he?'

Mother liked this very much, she smiled and nodded her head.

'I'm fine, thank you.'

She was lying, they had had a very bad argument only the other day. Why didn't she tell him that he did misbehave and that she needed help? She covered up for him, I didn't know why. She shouldn't. I wouldn't, I thought.

The two blue-eyed brothers sat down close to each other to chat intimately. It had puzzled me for a long time that both Father and Amo had blue eyes, and that all of Amo's children had blue eyes and fair hair, while we had black eyes and black hair. I once asked

Mother. She didn't know but said perhaps because she had black eyes and black hair we must have taken after her. But I didn't like myself, I was too black and hairy, while my cousins were fair and nice. Shaba had consoled me by saying that black people are nicer, warmer, sweeter, kinder and more humorous and white people are cold, hard, serious and unkind.

Shaba got the samovar, lit it, filled it with water and began preparing the tea. Mother was putting Vida to bed and Hamid was already yawning. Shaba made the fresh tea and let it brew.

'Are you following the news? Important events are taking place.'

'Well, everybody follows the news nowadays, every day there is a long queue outside the newspaper shop. People buy their paper first, then their bread.'

'What do you think is going to happen? Mosadegh is now being attacked by his own supporters, the petite bourgeoisie; Mulla Kashani and his clergy have deserted him. He *must* align himself with Herzhe Tudeh. The communists are the only chance for him.'

'Stop talking about Mosadegh and communism, come and have some tea, to refresh yourselves,' Shaba interrupted their conversation. They came closer and Shaba gave them fresh black tea in white shining glasses, small tumblers, curved in the middle, with golden rims. Jokes and laughter on personal issues followed while they were drinking tea.

I liked Amo very much, he was always very happy and whenever he came to visit us, we had fun; a few hours' precious fun. But Amo didn't talk to me, didn't ask me how I was: adults don't usually greet children. I was watching them, wanted to join in the conversation, talk and be talked to, but I wasn't sure that would be proper. Amo had only patted my head and said, 'Homa, my nice girl.' That was all. It wasn't enough.

Shaba asked Amo, 'How's the work? How's your boss? Did he recover his stolen carpets?'

'Fine, everything the same as usual, still behind the same old steering wheel. The boss is OK too. Always complaining about going bankrupt while he is making money all the time.'

Amo Salim was a chauffeur. His boss, who had a private marriage registry office, was a very rich man, a millionaire, although Amo told us that he had started his business with only very little money. His two children were studying in a public school in England and he was sending a lot of money to them regularly.

'He's a lucky devil, he found the stolen carpets, all four of them, valued at half a million toman.'

'How did he recover them so fast?' Father asked.

'Well, the thieves were fools, they didn't wait long enough and they tried to sell them in the bazaar. Of course those carpets were precious and the shopkeepers couldn't really put a value on them so they were suspicious.'

'What a bunch of fools, they couldn't even sell the stolen goods. They must have been beginners.'

'Yes, he's lucky, he has the right connections, the know-how, and the money to benefit himself. But he still grumbles about going bankrupt every other second. Would you believe that marrying others could be so profitable?'

'That is why the mullas are doing it – marriage and siegheh [temporary marriages which men can have as many of as they can afford] bring in money. It's a good business, the least labour makes maximum profit. We have a mulla in our street who got a child wife recently. I can't manage even with one wife, yet they multiply theirs.'

'Don't gossip behind people's back. It is a sin,' Shaba snapped at them.

'Yes teacher . . .' Father snapped back.

A few minutes later Father went out to the shop. Shaba saw her older son alone, so she began talking to him about herself, her health and the problems that she had. She would always talk to him about her bad health, getting old, and any upsets in the household.

'You know my eyes aren't any better, they're failing me, and my rheumatism is still the same. I'm getting old and it isn't nice to get old, you become dependent.'

'What does the doctor say? You can use Eby's bimeh [medical insurance], can't you?'

'Yes, I have tablets for my rheumatism and drops for my eyes; that is all they give you.'

'But didn't they have any effect? Didn't they make you feel better?'

'Well, not really. When I take the tablets I'm better for a short while but when the effect of the tablets wears off, I feel the same pain again. This is no cure. All they do is fob you off, the bloody doctors, especially the bimeh doctors. Treat you like an object. "Old woman, why are you still alive?", you know what I mean. It is

44

a very bad, bad system.'

'I can believe you. You need to go to a private doctor, but I haven't got any money with me this time. The next time I come I'll bring some.'

'Don't worry about me, it isn't important. I'm an old woman anyway. You shouldn't waste your money on me. Eby sometimes complains that he pays my total upkeep and you don't contribute anything. But I tell him that you have a difficult life too and I have chosen to live with him.'

Amo felt uncomfortable. He didn't like this kind of talk, he felt guilty about not paying any money towards Shaba's upkeep. Father always said that he was a mean man, he would only spend his wages for his family. He was soft and under the thumb of his wife and she didn't want him to give any money to Shaba.

Mother, who had been quiet for most of the time, came into the conversation, so Amo decided to change the subject.

'Are you all right? Being treated well?'

Mother just said, 'Well, yes, I suppose so, thank you, I'm fine.' She never complained to him. Perhaps she didn't trust him, he was Eby's brother.

'Well, just the other day he beat her up,' Shaba broke in. 'You know he has a foul temper, a long arm and a heavy hand for hitting. Swears all the time too.'

Mother was embarrassed, and bent her head. Perhaps Mother didn't want him to know about this even though she liked him. We heard the sound of the door, Father coming back. Shaba stopped talking but made a gesture with her eyes and eyebrows, to tell Salim that the situation was bad. Father walked in with a bottle of aragh in his hand. Mother brought them some glasses and they sat down drinking and chatting politics. Shaba started murmuring with annoyance and counting her rosary, begging forgiveness of God on their behalf for drinking impure liquor. Amo was polite and asked Mother to have a drink with them. She said she didn't like aragh, it was too strong for her. She preferred wine. She didn't leave the room, didn't go to bed. She just sat there watching them and listening to their conversation throughout the evening.

'How is life? . . . How are your wife and children?' Father asked Amo, offering him a glass of aragh.

'Fine, they're all right. Work is slower because of the daily demonstrations, and my boss is worried that this unrest is bad for registry office business. People don't want to get married so often now. He's a bit down . . .'

'Right . . . he must be . . . Who thinks of getting married when they have better things to do?'

'Um . . . how are things in the factory? Can you talk with the workers? . . . or move around easily?'

'Not bad . . . we've had a good response to our strike calls, and good news from other factories too. Pity the oil workers' strike was so bloody and the army moved in to shoot the workers, but . . . Still, I'm very careful when selling our papers at work. Luckily so far there hasn't been a problem. Mosadegh's big mistake has been to keep a ban on our party. We're his only chance . . . and . . .'

'Mosadegh doesn't trust the Russians – he thinks they've always had an eye on Iranian oil.'

'That's not the point. He claims to be fighting for a parliamentary democracy – to build a democratic state with freedom of speech, freedom of assembly – but he has banned the Communist Party.'

'But that isn't his fault. It's the Shah's and the army's. There is opposition to his own government . . . and, my God, even attacks on his life; and he still doesn't tackle the power of the Shah and his army; he just wants to limit their powers and strengthen Parliament, which is supposed to be strong anyway.'

'You're wrong. It *is* his fault. He is a petit bourgeois leader. He is a nationalist and a reformist. He is deceiving the masses. He thinks that America is not imperialist, and he thinks he can exploit the contradiction between British and American interests.' Father was angry, he gulped his aragh and started to light a cigarette. 'Your party from the very beginning supported the Soviet line and declared that Mosadegh was an American agent – a puppet of imperialism. How is it now you've changed your line and are supporting him and his policies?'

'Because he needs us, the help of our party, so we can unite against the Shah, the foreign imperialists and the army. Without this unity he cannot win. And you forget that Mosadegh is a very clever man, he was educated in Switzerland, he knows a bit about imperialist politics and he is a politician too. He doesn't want Iran to be either under English or Russian or American domination. Yes, he thinks that America is too far away to be a real threat to Iran; but he knows that Russia is too close for comfort – and the 1919 contract, which left part of our land under Soviet influence, is fresh in his memory.'

'No, you're wrong. We are a workers' party, the Soviet Union's support for us is because they are a workers' state too. We cannot win a progressive struggle without their help.'

'I don't think Stalin's Russia was so progressive . . . yes, I know, we won't agree on that. I think Stalin has very little to do with socialism in Iran. It was a mistake to have that huge Stalin remembrance day in Fosiyah Square, for instance. But let's not get heated about this . . . I agree that I haven't got a better alternative.'

'Look . . . British, American, Japanese imperialism isn't a joke. What is an old man, a young woman, a baby to them. They would sacrifice anybody, anything for their own interest and profit. The nationalisation of Iranian oil is just one small example of what is happening in the entire world. I give you this figure, think about it, see: British profit from our oil in 1950 alone was £150 million. Iran's income from our oil for the same year was only £3 million . . . We are the world's vital oil supplier and we have no control over our resources . . . and you go on criticising the Soviet Union.'

Amo was playing with his moustache, pulling at the hairs. He was silent, just muttered, 'No . . . No . . .'

I was puzzled by the talk between Father and Amo. I didn't understand what they were talking about. I tried hard to repeat their conversation in my mind but I didn't know whether they were for or against each other. The difference between them was that Amo was more relaxed and cheerful, talking calmly, while Father was serious, angry and pushy. But it seemed Amo respected Father because he knew more. I was very confused about all that, especially when it came to numbers and money. The sums were so huge, the numbers too big for me who couldn't count to more than a hundred and never had money more than a rial or two.

Eight

I woke up with lots of big words in my head, part of the conversation between my father and my uncle. Mother was feeding Vida, the room was clean and tidy, quiet and peaceful.

'Mum, what is communism?'

'What? Why do you want to know?'

47

'Well, what is it?'

'It's a system under which everyone has to work.'

'Oh, that's bad. I don't like working, especially at home.'

'Like the Soviet Union.'

'Father likes communism. Do you?'

'I hate it. Men are the same everywhere. They're bullies. Never trust what they say.'

'Why does Father like communism?'

'Because he wants more money; so he can spend it all on drink.'

Mother was sitting cross-legged, leaning against the wall, Vida sucking her breast peacefully and dozing. She looked content, so happy; she had no need to worry – everything was taken care of for her. She was secure in Mother's arms. Her hands were tiny and chubby, with closed fists. Shaba said babies with closed fists would turn out mean adults. Afagh must have had closed fists all the time. Vida's skin was so fresh, warm and blooming. She was naked when Mother changed her nappies. She had soft, round fat on her belly, legs and toes. I wanted to kiss her all over her body, to touch her and pinch those lovely nipples and rounded parts. Mother usually played with her when changing her, touching her all over, kissing her, talking sweetly to her. Vida loved it and moved her limbs, waved her hands, and laughed with her eyes, chuckling throughout. Did she feel ticklish when Mother cleaned her under her arms and in between her toes? She did laugh very loud. After she was cleaned, and changed into a fresh nappy, Mother would feed her and then she would gently sleep in her arms.

'Why do you look after Vida so much?'

'She's a baby and needs me.'

'But all the time?'

'Yes, all the time, you see . . .'

'What would happen if you left her alone one day? Did nothing for her?'

'I think she would die.' Mother's face turned dark and saddened.

'How do you know? Try it. Leave her alone for one day.'

'She would cry for me . . . cry very loud.'

'Don't answer her cries, go out. Go out and see your aunties, your friends.'

She laughed a bitter laugh. Her face looked unhappy.

'What about you? Would you have liked me to leave you? You don't understand. I will never leave Vida, not when she is so young, anyway. I once left your elder sister. You see, she was weaning, just a baby. I left not to come back again. She died. I was so remorseful that I came back.' She was grieved now. Her face wrinkled with pain. I was sorry too. So she had left; so I had had an older sister; she was dead. Oh, poor baby, poor girl. I wanted to ask more questions about my dead sister but my mother was miserable and I didn't feel like asking any more. It was a sad story.

I sneaked out into the street to play. Sara and her mother were sitting outside their house. The midsummer sun was high and hot, and our lane was busy. Sara's grandmother was sitting outside too. She was cleaning some beans in a tray. My grandmother rarely sat outside the house; she didn't speak to the neighbours either. She could have been Sara's grandmother's friend; it was a pity they didn't speak the same language. Sara's mother was squatting on the ground, holding her between her legs and looking through her hair. I was still not talking to her, but I wanted to know why her mother was searching her hair. It was thick, black and frizzy, closely knitted.

I got closer to her hair. I saw her mother pull out a little black insect which was stuck to the root of a hair and squash it between her two thumb nails. Little dots of blood were left on them. She went on searching.

I turned my head away. It was nasty. I had never seen those black insects. Why was she killing them? I walked away and stood under the balcony. I saw the children were playing at the bottom of the wide alley. Hamid, my brother, was there too, playing a game with a group of boys. I turned to Sara; she was still under her mother's thumbs, but she was being impatient and complaining to get out. She called out to her mother: 'How many more fleas are you going to catch? Do you want to kill them all now?' There must have been an army there, if she was still squashing her thumb nails together, I thought.

Whenever I wasn't speaking to Sara, I would talk and play with my other friends and exclude her. But I really wanted to make her jealous, then she would come and apologise to me. She in turn usually came to my friends to speak to them, but when she saw that I was ignoring her, she would go away. She would come back after a little while and try to catch my attention. She usually asked me to speak to her, then I would agree, but always with a little reluctance.

Today was different. I really wanted to know what on earth had

49

happened to her hair. I lingered on the corner. I was looking at the game that the boys were playing. They were running around and catching each other, holding long sticks in their hands and throwing them up and hitting them hard. Suddenly from the bottom of the alley, a young woman appeared, unveiled and handsome. She was elegantly dressed and her hair was nicely done. She was walking towards us. I recognised her. 'Ozra Khanoom,' I shouted to Sara, 'your sister is coming.' Sara was set free and she dashed down the road. Sara's mother stood up, straightened herself, and came up to see her too. Grandmother picked up the tray of beans and walked inside.

She came closer, now holding Sara's hand. She had a beautiful face, just like her picture in their room. Her lips were red, her eyebrows nicely trimmed, and she had red rouge on her cheeks. She talked with Sara and her mother and they all three passed under my watchful gaze and went through the door, inside the house. The door slammed shut.

Sara came to me and called me. 'I have money, look.' I looked and turned away. 'Don't you want to speak to me?' I remained silent.

'We can spend it. Come on . . .' She was holding a 10-rial note.

It was a lot of money. I had never had that much money to spend. I couldn't resist it.

'Where did you get it from?' I asked.

'My sister gave it to me. She also gave some money to my mother and my father. She has lots of money.'

'Yes, let's go and buy some sweets.'

We set off. Sara bought a red cock lolly for herself and a green one for me. The blind woman searched through her money and touched each coin with her fingertips to check its value. How could she recognise the coins when she couldn't see? She even knew the colours sometimes. Oh, she must be very intelligent. Sara got her change and told me, while sucking her lolly, that she too didn't understand how she could give her the right money.

'It must be hard work, you know, being blind and still earning your living,' I told Sara. She heard me but was more interested in her lolly, and only shook her head. We walked back towards home sucking our lollies. Just outside Mulla's house there were lots of bricks, some planks of wood, a mound of earth, and a big barrel.

'He must be building something inside his house,' Sara said.

'Yes, perhaps a little room for his wife.'

We looked around, removed some planks, and put them on the

bricks. I had an idea. 'Sara, let's make a see-saw.'

'Yes, what a good idea.'

She soon chose a long plank and I put the barrel down. We moved the plank to the top of the barrel. She sat on one end and told me to sit on the other. She was heavier than me and I had to push hard to make her go up in the air. We went up and down, laughing, pleased with our invention. Suddenly Mulla came out of his house, wrapped in his black robe, and called out:

'Disgraceful girls, you shouldn't be out playing. Why doesn't your mother look after you properly? Shameful! And how loud you are laughing. You should be ashamed of yourselves.'

We ran home – the sight of him gave us a fright, never mind his reproach. We hid in our lane and waited until some time had passed, then came out of our hiding place and peeped down the alley. There was no sign of him, but our see-saw had been taken over by two big boys. I got mad.

'Get off; we made it ourselves.'

'No, it's ours now.' One of them pushed me away. Sara was tackling the other boy: 'Get down, I made it.'

I grabbed his T-shirt and pulled it. He came down, held me and hit me hard on the head. I kicked him, he pulled my hair as hard as he could. Pain overcame me, and I screamed. He started to hit me again. My arms and legs were all battered and the roots of my hair hurt. I ran home crying and holding my head. Tears streamed down my face and I was howling. I walked into our house. Mother got angry, seeing me whining. I complained, 'That big boy Akhar hit me.' I wanted sympathy and support like Sara's mother gave her. She always told the big boys off and complained to their mothers. But my mother came towards me, grabbed me by my arms and squeezed them hard. She lifted me up and bit my head with her sharp teeth, like the edge of a knife pushed into my skull. The pain shot through my skull, as if it was cut in two. She slapped me.

'It's your fault. If you hadn't gone out to play with the others you wouldn't have been beaten up. It's your fault, your fault. Stay at home, I always tell you, stay at home . . .'

I held my bruised head and crept to my corner, crumpled my body in my arms and cried bitterly but quietly. By now I had learned to cry noiselessly, with tears just pouring down my face, bottling the pain inside. I had forgotten that Akhar had beaten me up, and why. My body felt bruised all over, the roots of my hair were painful. I fell asleep.

Father said it was too hot to sleep inside the room. It was mid summer. We put our bedding in the yard. Sleeping in the yard was more fun, looking at the sky and the stars, and falling asleep with their imprint behind our eyelids. But that night I was too miserable. I was lying down staring at the sky. The words came back to me and hurt me like that big bump on my head. Perhaps that bite-mark from my mother's teeth would stay on my skull till I was grown up.

'It's your fault. If you hadn't gone out, you wouldn't have been beaten up. Stay at home, I always tell you, stay at home. It's a safer place.'

The pain hurt and the words hurt too. I didn't understand them. Why? I lay there and looked at the black sky and asked myself why. Whenever I was told big words and difficult sentences that I did not understand, I repeated them many times to memorise them. Perhaps one day I would learn what they meant.

Nine

Mother was in the guest room. This was unusual, because it was only opened for cleaning or for when we were going to entertain guests there. This was our best room. It had a nice carpet in it and a trunk in one corner where we kept our china and Mother kept her valuables and our best clothes. There were some glass cups shining on the mantelpiece and some photos of our family. It was kept very clean and tidy. Mother swept it and dusted it regularly, shining the glass tea cups individually and meticulously.

Mother was sitting cross-legged on the carpet, leaning against the wall and reading. Everything everywhere was quiet. Peace and calm was scarce in our place, but now it seemed as if everyone was taking a break. I went to Mother. I rarely saw her with a book. The room was dim although the sun was pouring down outside. Mother stopped reading and looked at me for a second, then went on reading again. I crawled to her noiselessly and sat beside her, so as not to disturb her peace. I looked at her book. It was a small book with small writing – I couldn't read it. I wanted to know what it was but I also didn't want to interrupt her. I just went on looking at the pages, and at the carpet. It was a deep blue and red one, and as in most Persian carpets, the patterns wove and curved around themselves and met again. Mother closed the book and put it in her lap.

'What are you reading? I hardly ever see you with a book.'

'It is Hafez's poetry; I like his poetry. Why don't you go and play?'

'No, I want to stay here. Please read me a bit.'

'Well . . .' She seemed reluctant.

'Please, go on . . .'

'All right. It's a lovely poem.' She smiled.

I leaned on her soft body. I was so aware of her body close to mine. She hadn't the chador on, just her cotton dress. She looked very different. It was like seeing her for the first time, seeing her the way she wanted to be. She was content. She was reading a poem that she liked and enjoyed. She read:

> Wild of mine, chanting a love-song
> cup in hand, locks disarrayed,
> Cheek beflushed, wine-overcome
> vesture awry, breast displayed.
>
> With a challenge in that eye's
> glance, with a love-charm on the lip,
> Come my love, sit by my bedside
> in the dim midnight shade.
>
> O'er my ear bending, my love
> spake in a sad voice and a low,
> 'Is it thus, spite of the old years,
> lover mine, slumber – bewrayed?'
>
> To the wise comes there a cup,
> fired of the night, pressed to the lip;
> And he bow not to the Wine Creed,
> be he writ Love's renegade.

She was being nice to me and reading me some of her favourite poems. For once she had time to read some poetry. My belly went warm with joy, but I didn't want it to come out, didn't want to express it in case it disappeared too soon. I wanted the joy and the warmth to stay there in my belly for a long time.

> Not all the sum of earthly happiness

Is worth the bowed head of a moment's pain,
And if I sell for wine my holy dervish dress,
Worth more than what I sell is what I gain!
Land where my lady dwells, thou holdest me
Enchanted; else Fars were but a barren soil,
Not worth the journey over land and sea,
      Not worth the toil!

Down in the quarter where they sell red wine,
My holy carpet scarce would fetch a cup –
How brave pledge of piety is mine,
Which is not worth a goblet foaming up!

All my pleasure is to sip
Wine from my beloved's lip;
I have gained the utmost bliss –
God alone be praised for this.

Fate, my old and stubborn foe,
Never let my darling go:
Give my mouth the golden wine
And her lips incarnadine.

(Clerics bigoted for God,
Elders who have lost the road –
These have made a tale of us
'Drunken sots and bibulous'.

Let th' ascetic's life be dim,
I will nothing have of him;
If the Mulla will pious be,
God forgive his piety!)

Mother closed her eyes and recited a poem by heart:

Here with a Loaf of Bread beneath the Bough,
A Flask of Wine, a Book of Verse – and Thou
Beside me singing in the Wilderness –
And Wilderness is Paradise enow.

Mother looked very calm, pleased and content. We sat there for a quiet short moment. I couldn't wait any longer; although I hadn't understood most of it I had enjoyed the sound of it and its musical rhymes.

54

'It sounds so nice to my ears, so beautiful. What does it mean? It's so lively and musical . . .'

'Oh . . . yes. I like Hafez's poems. I like his ideas of beauty, pleasure, and his criticism of Islamic morality, his attack on the clerics' hypocrisy. It's a pleasure to read these poems. I make a wish with them too. I like Khayyam as well, but Hafez's poetry has much deeper meaning and is much more philosophical. He is also much more outspoken on the repression of the time.' It was difficult to understand Mother all the time; it seemed she was talking to herself. She saw my puzzled eyes and stopped.

'Where did you learn it?'

'At school. You will learn it too. That is why I want you to go to school.'

'Will I be taught poetry too?'

'Yes, if you stay on and continue school.'

'I will. I want to. What else did you learn in school?'

'I learnt maths, I was very bad at it; English and a bit of French and Persian literature.'

'You know so much, such nice and different things.'

Mother's hand touched my hair. How warm. I wanted the hand to stay there and not to move.

'What is English and French?'

'In school they teach you foreign languages. Arabic at some schools, English and French at others.'

'Did you like school?'

'Yes, I liked it. It is better if you go to school and continue till you finish it. I know your father and Shaba disagree, but you must try. They think all a woman should do is find a husband as quickly as possible. But it's not true. What good did it do me or any other woman? Girls must be educated first and foremost, that is what my grandmother believed too. When you were born, she said the Muslim tradition which buries the girl's umbilical cord in the house and the boy's in the garden should be the other way round: girls should be educated to want a career of their own, and never stay at home, and boys should do all the things that girls are supposed to do at home. She buried your cord outside. I think school is just the beginning.'

'So did you have a nice grandmother too?'

'She was very strong and managed all our family's business affairs. I liked her very much.'

My mother was stroking my hair. Her voice was strong and it drew me to her. I didn't understand everything that she said, but I liked it. She was encouraging and loving, so unusual. She never had time to read. She didn't have the time or the patience to be loving or encouraging. She was usually so bitter, so blank, so indifferent. We sat quietly, leaning on one another. I was small, only as big as her knees folded up. It was a precious moment. I hoped there would be more times like this for us. I really wished for more of this closeness.

I heard Shaba calling Mother angrily, 'What on earth are you doing? Where are you hiding?' She came in and saw us. 'Reading? What good does it do you except weaken your eyesight?'

'Why are you shouting for me? What's wrong?' Mother asked angrily.

'Why are you wasting your time in here? What is the good of those books when your work is waiting for you in the kitchen?' Shaba demanded, still angry. I was annoyed. She had interrupted our nice time together.

'Can't I have a moment of peace? I have never rested in this house.' Mother was angry with her too.

'You're a lady compared to many other women.'

'A lady . . .' Mother mocked and went on to answer Shaba back and continue the argument. Shaba was unfair, critical and unhappy with Mother's conduct. They often argued a lot, sometimes bitter, violent arguments which went on for a long while. But usually things were normal between them again in a few hours – they had to be. Except that they mistrusted each other because one was the wife of the husband and one the mother of the son.

Shaba was going to stay with her elder son for the day. I begged her to take me – I liked my uncle's children, my cousins, and they had more freedom to play in the street. But she refused and said, 'Your father won't let me take you. Some other time when I have asked his permission first.' It was a pity. I liked going out so much. We never went out visiting people or places. It was so boring staying in the house with the same things, day in day out.

Shaba gave Mother some money and told her what to buy and how to cook the dinner. 'Buy the meat, beans, tomatoes and potatoes. Chop the meat, fry it with onion, clean the grit from the beans, wash them, and then let them boil with the meat and onion for a few hours. Add the tomatoes and potatoes half an hour before eating time. But make sure you do it right, or Eby will be angry.'

Father always gave the housekeeping money to Shaba, as Mother was considered too inexperienced to be trusted with it. Today, she was pleased that she would be in control for a short time, and she carefully put the money away. Shaba reminded her, 'Spend it wisely.'

Mother asked Afagh to watch Vida, and put on the chador and took the shopping bag, telling me to go with her. I held on to her chador and followed her. In the butcher's, the stripped, bloody cow was hung upside-down. Its head was on the wooden mantel for sale. The butcher was a big man with a black moustache. His white overall was blood-stained. Mother pointed to a part of the cow's leg, and he cut it with a long sharp knife. After she had bought it, we went to the grocer's. In the grocer's shop, I asked for a toffee. Mother grumbled. 'Perhaps the money won't be enough, wait.' I asked again. There were some pennies left. She agreed to buy some toffee but told me we would share it. I said yes and we left the shop.

After she had finished the shopping, she took a deep breath of relief. 'Oh, I'm always afraid that the money won't last and I'll have to ask the shopkeeper if I can pay him later. Then I'd have to avoid that shop until I got the money,' she said nervously. 'Let's go to the little park by the railway square, sit on a bench and eat our toffee.' Mother liked sweets too and she was free today.

'Oh, yes, let's go,' I happily agreed.

In the park Mother put down the heavy shopping bag and sighed with relief. She sat down on a wooden bench; I sat next to her. We shared the toffee. There was nobody waiting for her at home, so she could feel relaxed and take her time. Mother was thoughtful, as usual. The park was crowded. On every bench there was a family, with four or five children, most of them small. The midsummer heat was extremely hot and dry, sweaty and sleepy. The park was cooler than the roads.

Mother didn't like crowds or noise. I looked at the grass, the roses, geraniums and pansies. They were very colourful, with their yellow or purple spots on the blue petals. There were lots of them in the spring and summer, but they didn't live long. Mother wasn't talking; she looked sad. I wanted her to talk to me, to say something. Why was she so thoughtful? What was bothering her? She was free now for a little while, but still unhappy. I wanted to know, to talk to her, pull her out of her thoughts. I was happy, I liked the park, I liked being out, I wanted to tell her, to ask her; but I didn't. I didn't interrupt her peace. I didn't say anything. Why was she always so thoughtful? Why didn't she talk to me?

At home, Mother was soon busy cooking. She hadn't cooked much before as Shaba did the cooking all the time. She had helped, but not done it alone. Shaba was usually around. Today Mother was all by herself and didn't seem to be enjoying it either. Once, I caught the flame too high and once it was too low, nearly dying. The cooker was very old and in pieces and Mother didn't know the right temperature it needed and how long for. She was especially confused when it came to preparing Vida's food and changing her at the same time.

The first thing Father asked was, 'Where is Shaba?' and 'What is there to eat?' Father didn't know where Shaba was, as she didn't need to ask his permission to go out. He sat down, had his wash, threw off his dirty socks and handkerchief, and disappeared behind the newspaper.

20,000 LEFTIST ANTI-SHAH DEMONSTRATORS DEMAND DISSOLUTION OF MAJALES

ESTABLISHMENT OF REVOLUTIONARY TRIBUNALS TO TRY THOSE RESPONSIBLE FOR MURDER OF CHIEF OF POLICE

LAW FOR ELIMINATING 'CLASS PRIVILEGES'

INDONESIA WITHOUT A GOVERNMENT – SUKARNO MAY NEGOTIATE FOR COALITION WITH EXTREME LEFT

158,642 KENYANS SIGN WITH BLOOD AGAINST BRITISH TAKEOVER OF 16,700 SQ. MILES OF THEIR MOST FERTILE LAND – 'LAND IS LIFE'

Father turned the pages over; there were many pictures of people demonstrating, shouting, carrying flags and banners. There were also large pictures of a policeman, blood all over him, by a river in a valley. Father was sad looking at the pictures. He was swearing and biting his lips and shaking his head. He gazed at them for a long time.

Hamid went to him, coming in from playing in the street. Father put him on his lap and began to talk sweetly to him: 'How is my son?' He kissed him a few times, took his willy in his fingers and admired it.

'What a nice fat willy. How is it growing? Is it being fed properly? Growing fat and big. It must be soon, you're becoming a man, my son, my dear son.'

I was watching them. Father usually admired Hamid like that; and always when there was a quarrel in the house, he would swear on Hamid's willy: 'To hell with everything. To hell with you. May you all be sacrificed to my son's fat willy.' Hamid got treated like this every night.

'Let's sit in the yard – it's too stuffy inside,' Father told Mother.

Mother pulled the rug from the sitting room and put it in the yard. Father moved on to it with his newspaper still open in his hand.

'Is supper ready?' he asked.

'Well, I think so.'

'Bring it then. I'm starving.'

Mother brought the huge round copper tray and put it in front of him. She laid the plates, bread, all neat and ready. The abgosht pot was put before Father. He put the paper away and looked at it. 'It's colourless.' Mother ignored him. I was sitting with Hamid near the hoze; he was next to Father. Grandmother's place was empty. Father poured the gravy out into a big bowl and we all began cutting the bread into small pieces and adding them to the juice. Father mixed it when it was well soaked and gave us our shares.

Was he talking to himself or to Mother? He wasn't looking at her. He was eating. 'Why isn't it salted?' He added some and ate another mouthful. But it seemed he had difficulty in swallowing it. 'It's tasteless. Did you add salt? Spices?'

'I think so . . .' Mother wasn't sure. It wasn't as tasty as Shaba's but it was edible. Father swallowed the mouthfuls and was getting angrier. I was beginning to get nervous. Luckily he finished his plate and pulled forward the meat and peas to mash them. He took the wooden masher, held it up, and brought it down on the contents of the pot. A few chickpeas jumped out of the pot and landed on the copper tray. Mother was still eating. She usually ate slowly and finished after everyone. She saw it, and the spoon stopped moving in her hand. She was aware. Father looked at her angrily, took a few peas in his hand and squeezed them between his fingers. The chickpeas were not cooked. He took a fork and pushed it into a piece of meat. It didn't go in.

'The meat is not cooked either. What the hell have you been doing today?'

'It has been boiling all afternoon.'

'Since when?'

'Well, two o'clock.'

'Why hasn't it cooked then? Did you leave it low? Have you been out?' He was getting furious. I was shaking.

'No, I haven't been out . . . how can I?' He looked at me. Oh God, the park. I wanted to disappear. His eyes were getting larger and larger, his cheekbones sticking our sharper.

'I don't know how to cook,' she murmured. 'I turned the flame down, it was too high.'

'You've been in this house nearly ten years now, and you can't cook. Shame on you, useless, worthless woman. What on earth are you good for? You can't even cook a meal.'

'I didn't cook in my father's house.' Mother was wrapping her chador around herself tighter, as if wanting to hide.

'My God! Why don't you learn?'

'I have enough to do, I haven't got time to learn anything else.' Mother's voice was low and mumbling.

'Fuck your education, fuck your father's house that . . .' Father was shouting in the yard now.

'Don't insult my . . .'

It was still dusk, but getting darker. I was shaking. Hamid's eyes grew larger and he was moving slowly backwards, away from the food tray. Father was now in a rage and swearing.

'I work twelve hours a day, then come home exhausted . . . to eat this shit!' He held the copper tray in his hands, veins bulging on his arms and throat. In a maddened fury, he lifted it up and threw it with force out into the hoze. The copper tray circled and lurched, then splashed down hard on to the surface of the pond. Water splashed out on to the yard, soaking the dry cement around the hoze. The tray, with food, plates and spoons, was sinking to the bottom of the pond. We scattered. I stood in the corner of the yard between the two brick walls. Afagh came out on to her balcony, looked at us and the hoze, and went back indoors. Hamid had disappeared into the toilet. I saw Mother, wrapped in her black chador, being punched and trampled by my father. In the dim light of the sitting room, under her black veil, she looked squashed, beaten, like a cushion, shaken and flattened like when Shaba made the mattresses, filling them with cotton and beating them till they were completely flattened, soft and cosy to sleep on.

Chickpeas and pieces of bread and the wooden masher with its long handle and round, thick tip, were floating in the water of the hoze. I thought of the poor goldfish – they couldn't swim under the weight of that heavy copper tray, couldn't eat the meat and the chickpeas. Their water was polluted. Perhaps they had been struck on their heads by the copper tray, split open with blood everywhere. They might be dead, and would soon float to the surface with their heads broken open. Poor goldfish.

My legs were wobbly, shaking like jelly. I wanted to hide. I wanted the earth to open beneath my feet and swallow me up. Mother was moaning like a pigeon, shot in the wing. Her crying pounded in my ears and tore my nerves to shreds. She was like a wounded bird, wings flapping; shot at, moaning with a bitter cry.

Ten

The night was dark and hard. The morning began grey and dull; we stayed under the blankets, half asleep and half awake, one eye open until Father got up, angry and irritable, and Mother gave him his breakfast and saw him off to work. Mother was moving slowly about, getting our breakfast ready. She was black and blue, and looked cold and hard, no expression on her face. I felt black and blue too. I reluctantly dragged myself out of bed; I wanted to sleep on for a long time but I had been woken earlier than usual.

The room was half dark and our shadows were ghostly on the wall. I went out into the yard in search of fresh air. Light was breaking through, faint and colourless; dawn was coming, pale and yellow. It was getting pink and red and redder. Appearing in the distance, the sun grew larger and brighter. It was the colour of blood, red like fire, as if burning, as if the dawn were setting the day ablaze.

In the twilight, the yard felt vacant and cold. I sat on the cold, hard cement edge of the hoze. It looked sick, sick with food floating on the surface: the chickpeas, tomatoes and masher. The long handle of the masher was half submerged under water. Looking at it made me ill. Were the goldfish alive? How could they be? I cared for them and I still wanted them to be alive. But the water looked sickly. I put my hands in it; it was cold on my fingers. I swished my hands around a bit underwater, without much hope or enthusiasm. Perhaps the goldfish were afraid to come to the surface, if they were still alive, in case they might be hit again. The water was dull and greyish. How could anything live in it?

Tiny little orangy-red spots appeared beneath the surface of the water. Swimming up, they became brighter till the shiny scales appeared and the heads gulped air. Oh, I was glad to see them, they were alive. They had survived it all. How incredible! So the copper tray hadn't broken their heads open. I was so afraid, I chased them beneath the water to try and catch them, but they swam away, deep down where it was safe from me. They had a good place to hide away; I didn't.

Mother took the wooden masher out of the water and tried to clean the hoze of the other bits and pieces. She had a long stick in her hand and poked around in the water, swearing and grumbling beneath her breath about how hopeless things were. She was still upset; she left the hoze and went indoors.

Mother had started the day's housework as if last night's events hadn't happened; perhaps she wanted to lose herself in the daily chores. Her face was still puffy and wrinkled with the marks of the slaps and beatings, and it looked as if the skin beneath was filled with tears. She went around looking miserable and grieved. When she fed Vida, she hit her for being hungry. She shouted at me to get the breakfast plates ready. I moved like a mouse, afraid of her pain and fearful of her anger, doing exactly as she asked, always watching her so as not to put a step wrong. Hamid was so apprehensive that he kept away all the time, squatting in a corner of the yard and staring dumbly into space. Mother's big, black eyes had shrunk and looked half closed, half hidden.

She threw Vida in her cot and slapped her and swore at her for crying. 'To hell with you, sucking me dry and still wanting more.'

Afagh came out of her room and down the stairs, looking at my mother. She sat halfway down the stairs, and began questioning Mother, as she was very curious to know what had happened. I knew that Afagh didn't like my father from the remarks she had often made – she didn't like his arguments, his loud, angry voice, and his swearing all the time. She didn't like the filthy overalls which Mother had to wash all the time. She liked nice clothes. She was always telling Mother to dress up in nice, clean clothes. Her son's clothes were always freshly washed and ironed. She told us not to swear and not to use bad language. She often told Hamid off when he was swearing and being naughty. She liked money very much and said it was the most important thing in our lives. She told my mother to save her money for herself for hard days. Then she would not need the help of others.

'Eby only wants your money, don't be a fool,' she would say. She herself wore dresses which were very old, but clean. She had a pair of black leather shoes and a black leather bag, both very old and out of fashion, but she wore them all the time. The shoes were half-boots, coming up to her ankles, with thick heels, and laces on the front. They were fat and thick at the toe, and looked very funny: we made fun of her shoes and joked about them.

Mother came into the yard, put the plates down by the hoze, pulled the clean clothes from the line and crumpled them under her arm. She looked bent, as if she were trying to hide her face under her chador. Afagh was sitting on the stairs. She looked clean and fine, as usual. Her eyebrows were knitted; she wanted to talk to Mother and find out more about last night, but Mother was not in a mood for talking. She tried to ignore Afagh. Mother looked lost; she paced a few steps up the yard, then back again. Pumping the water, she suddenly stopped and looked at the mess floating on the surface. She sat on the edge of the hoze and tried to pick out the pieces with her hand. Afagh was asking questions; Mother didn't want to answer. She just said, 'Well . . . yes . . . I don't know . . . Ohh . . . Ah . . .' Sun was spreading over the yard, warming everything.

'He threw everything into the hoze; he must have been mad . . . all my body is bruised . . . as if it's been minced, mashed up. All my bones are aching. All because of some salt and uncooked meat. He doesn't even care about his children, making such a show in front of them. They'll pick it up from him and grow up even worse . . . He was mad, so angry, like a wild bull . . . it was awful . . . Ah . . . Ah, stamping on me as if I wasn't made of flesh and blood . . . To hell with the man, to hell with you. He's a brute, a selfish, pig-headed brute. How can anyone be so inhuman? So insensitive? So careless in front of his children? He's got no compassion. Is this the way men care for their wives and children?' Mother shook her head in despair, looking blank. 'What an example he sets for them; they will learn all this.' She pointed to Hamid sitting in the corner of the yard. 'God have pity on them. He isn't a man. Beating a woman is not manly at all . . . What a terrible life. I'm ruined . . . all for nothing . . . What choice do I have? Where can I go? Where is there help?'

'You blame yourself now,' Afagh interrupted. 'You complain, but we warned you; we told you, you wouldn't listen. You chose him; this is the result of your choice; this is the man you wanted.'

'How did I know? How could I look into the future? I'm not a prophet. How did I know my life would turn out to be like this?'

Afagh was pointing her fingers at her. She was quick to blame her. I knew that I didn't like her but didn't know why. Perhaps this was it.

'We warned you . . . all those suitable rich men who wanted to marry you. You were blind . . . you refused them all. Look what you have chosen . . . a brute of a worker. What do you expect from a penniless worker? Brutality is part of their nature.'

'I don't know. I don't know what to say . . . it must be the fate that's written on my forehead . . . my poor miserable fate.'

'And you listen to his talk; reading the paper with his fancy ideas. He wants a workers' government! Thank God they have no power – give them a rope and they'll hang us all.'

'To hell with his ideas; they're all bullshit. My life is ruined; it's my fate, my miserable fate.'

'Your fate, yes, and you made it. You made your own bed and now you must lie on it. What can you do now with three kids?'

'There's no way out . . . nothing I can do . . . I've made my bed and I must lie on it. I have to go on for the sake of these three kids, these three fucking kids . . . his kids. He cheated me, he ruined my life.'

'This is the result of all your sacrifices for him; everything you did for him; turning your back on your family . . . all the wealth and inheritance you lost because of him. Can he appreciate any of that? No wonder the Turks are called donkeys. The word suits them fine.'

'I've ruined my life . . . it was my choice . . . I've made myself miserable for the rest of my life. There's no way out, no return. I must bear the brunt of it. This is it for me.' Mother bent her head, resigned. Her cheekbones stuck out sharp and hard. Her eyes were empty of expression, cold and hard. Her face was wrinkled, stony, black and blue.

I went to the hoze to try and pick out the pieces of food, as Mother had stopped doing it. I picked up a floating chickpea and threw it in the gutter; a piece of meat, which was soft and rotting. There was too much to do, it was too much for me to clean alone. I couldn't do it.

Eleven

Our alley was so narrow that when Sara and I sat on the ground facing each other, with our backs to the wall and our legs stretched out, our feet would touch. We were playing five stones, first her, then me, putting the stones down and throwing them up and catching them. We played for a while and got bored with it and

64

left the stones on the ground. Sara turned around and came to my side and sat close to me. We began chatting and whispering. The early morning sun was now much hotter. We had taken refuge in the shade of the wall, beneath the honeysuckle.

'Sara, what do you want to be when you grow up?'

'A housewife.'

'Me too. Shaba says when I grow up I'll get married and have a husband and children. I like that.'

Sara was throwing her marbles about at random and picking them up.

'Yes, I want to get married when I am a woman. I want to be a woman soon.'

'Shaba says you wear a beautiful all-white lace dress, long down to your toes, and hold your husband's hand and smile all the time. She says it is very nice and I will be very, very happy.'

'Yes, just like my sister. She has many pictures of her wedding. She is so beautiful and happily smiling . . . But now her husband has left her.'

'That's bad; what does she do then?'

'She's been left with a baby, and she has to work.'

'What kind of work?'

'I don't know really . . . something like dancing.'

'Dancing? . . . I didn't know that was a job . . . My father dances too, but he only does it at our family weddings. He's so good at it, ah . . . he jumps like an acrobat . . . He learned it in Russia.'

'I haven't seen a man dancing.'

'He's very good, really. I like his dancing and the music too – very noisy and happy.'

Sara's two brothers ran into the alley and told her: 'We have a good idea; we want to go to the railway to see the trains. Do you want to come?'

'Yes, of course.'

'Come on, Homa.'

'I'm not sure . . . shall I tell Shaba?'

'No, let's just go,' Sara tried to persuade me. I wanted to go with them but I couldn't without letting somebody know. Mother would get mad if she needed me and couldn't find me. I tossed the idea over in my mind. I wanted to go.

'But I should tell Mother. If I do tell her, she won't let me. If I go and she finds out, I'll be in trouble. I'll be beaten when we come back,' I told Sara.

'No, don't worry, we'll come back early. She won't know about it,' she told me, sounding very certain.

'Perhaps . . . all right. I'm not sure . . . well, let's go.' I followed them, taking the risk. Hamid saw us all going and joined us too. Just before we left Javady Alley, Farid and Farideh, who were playing together, came towards us and also joined us. Now we were seven. Hamid was the youngest. I held his hand and Sara, my hand. Hassan and Hosein, Sara's brothers, were walking in front of us, leading the way. Farid and Farideh were side by side next to us and we began to talk. I liked Farideh but I didn't see her much because she lived further away from us and she always played with her brother, when she wasn't helping her mother. She was the same age as me but a bit smaller. She was a gentle, beautiful girl. Everyone thought her beautiful because, unlike us, she had a white skin and fair hair.

'Will you go to school this year?' I asked her.

'I don't know. My mother is going to ask a school.'

'If you are, come to my school,' I suggested to her.

'Look, we're on the main road!' somebody shouted. We had passed through the tangle of our small alleys into bigger lanes, and now the roads were wide, the cars passing fast, beside the slow horse-drawn carts. The gutters were wide too. We crossed one; the water was black and rubbish was rolling in it. We walked by the side of the park till we came to the railway square. Here there were many people. It was crowded and chaotic. Crowds were buzzing everywhere: people queuing for buses, men sitting outside tea houses, chatting or smoking the waterpipe. Many were standing at the corners of the road, by the shops, talking or just looking around. Some of them were doing things, others were just walking, but it seemed most were waiting, wondering. I was afraid in case I saw somebody who knew me, but Sara's brothers were leading the way a few yards in front of us, and they were not afraid. They must have been to these places before. When we came to a crowd, I just lowered my head and avoided looking at the people. I didn't like being in a crowd, I was hoping all along that nobody would recognise me. If somebody did, they could tell my parents and my life would be awful.

Soon we crossed the square. I was still holding Hamid's hand in mine. Luckily nobody recognised me, and we steered clear of the speeding cars. I looked up and saw the yellow statue of the Shah on its large column. The bronze was shining under the glowing sun. It was very high up, beyond anybody's reach. How had they put it up so high? I walked by and still turned back to see him. He looked very young and handsome, very serious. Why didn't Father like him?

While we were walking we saw big, red and black writing on the walls, the buildings on the ground and even on the Shah's column. I asked Hosein and he said that it was all about the Shah, the oil and Mosadegh: WE WANT NATIONALISATION OF THE OIL; IMPERIALISM OUT; DEATH TO THE SHAH, BRITAIN, THE USA.

We passed the main building of the railway station and the large white marble steps. Doors were swinging open and closing as passengers moved in and out with large suitcases. Hosein, leading the way, said, 'We can't get through the main entrance. Let's find another way. Follow me,' he said with pride.

We took Javadieh Road, and walked by the long wire fence which ran between us and the train tracks. We went on still, in three rows, Hassan and Hosein first, Sara and me with Hamid next behind them, Farid and Farideh behind us.

This street led to the slaughter house, to the crowded slums of Javadieh. Here the streets were crowded with numerous children. The air smelled of blood, heat and refuse. It was thick with the smell of shit and blood. We came to a corner where there were some trees and bushes. Here the wire fence was leaning on the trees. Hassan and Hosein stopped and said that this was the best place and we could cross over to the train track. I wasn't sure, but soon he climbed up the wire fence and got hold of the tree and stood on a strong branch. 'Now, come on then. It's easy,' he told everybody. Hassan followed him, then Farideh and Farid, while I looked on. We all helped each other to climb up the wire fence and then climb down the tree to the other side, except me. I was afraid. I didn't know how to climb up. I stood there and dithered. Sara had no problem, with a bit of a struggle and a bit of help, but more than anything her keen enthusiasm. She was up the tree in a minute. I didn't dare. My legs were shaking. Sara was shouting across the fence, 'Come on, it's fun, you can make it.'

She was very encouraging but I couldn't. 'Me? How . . . It's so high up . . . the fence doesn't look safe.' I was nervous. They were looking at me, smiling and encouraging. I looked at them, fearful and anxious. Could I make it? I thought, while my heart was going soft and crumbling.

Hassan climbed up from the other side and helped me on to the wire. I began holding the fence with my shaky hands and found a foothold for my wobbly feet but couldn't move any further. Like a strangled cat, I gripped the wire with my hands and hung in mid-air, panicking. He soon bent down and took my hand and pulled me up.

'You're lazy, you know, not adventurous at all,' he told me, proud of having helped me. Once up the tree, holding his hand, I felt safe although I didn't like his remark. Climbing down was easy and I was glad that I didn't need his help.

Before us there was a large open space covered with tracks, and some small, unused trains were in the distance. Javadieh Bridge was not far away to the left. Under the bridge on the same side there was a little house. I wanted to cross the track line to get to it, but I was afraid, although already everybody was scattered around doing something. Hamid was following Hassan and Hosein; they were going towards one of the disused trains. Sara was searching behind some bushes. 'Come on, Homa, let's see what there is around here.' I went to her.

'I'm really afraid in case a train comes.'

'Don't be silly, we can hear it.'

'But it may be too late, and we'll be run over. Imagine what trouble we will get into with our parents if we have any accidents here.'

'It can't happen. This is the trains' garage; they come to a stop in here and we can hear them for miles.' Sara had found a big stick and was poking it about on the earth, in the bushes. 'Let's find a tree and climb it,' she said, looking bored with the stick.

'I'm afraid of trees; I don't like climbing.'

'You can learn, don't be such a baby,' she told me, as if impatient with my fears and uncertainties.

'I'm not; I just don't want to fall down.'

'You won't fall down if you hold on tight.' She walked a few yards and told me, 'Come and hold my feet then.'

'Me? . . . All right . . . but you're heavy.'

'Just lift me up . . . try.'

While she hung on a branch I held her feet and lifted her up. Soon she managed to get a hold on the branches and climb up. I was so tempted to follow her, I tried one step up, took a branch, but I felt shaky and unstable. I couldn't trust my feet, they weren't strong enough. Sara was sitting on a branch up there, encouraging me. But I couldn't climb up.

'I don't like it, it's scary, looking down frightens me. I think I'm going to fall down all the time,' I said, moving back a bit and sitting down. I had given up.

The boys were up the train trying its doors and windows. They were searching through it, hanging out through the windows and shouting noisily with joy. Hosein had his catapult with him, as usual. He sat on the roof of the train and pointed it at passers-by across the bridge and at the children in the trees. He often hurt children like that and I hated it.

Farid and Farideh were running across the tracks a long way away.

I wasn't adventurous. It was hot and dusty. Between the tracks, the earth was dry and crumbling, spraying dust as soon as we walked on it. It was still and there was no sound of a train. The tracks were hot and grimy, everything around looked disused, rusty and metallic.

Looking under the scorching sun, I remembered one hot day when my father took me to Javadieh to his friend's house. Most of his Turkish friends lived and worked there. My mother had dressed me up. I had a short, cotton dress on; it was soft and cool. Going through the dirt track when sun and dust were mixed together, I noticed the men sitting around, or selling meat near the slaughter house. Some still had their bloody aprons on. Father said they were butchers, bloody from cutting off the heads of cows and sheep. I didn't like the look of them. They were looking me up and down. Perhaps my dress was too short and my legs were showing. I was safe with my father, holding his hand, but still I didn't like them looking at us like that. Perhaps it would have been better if I had worn a chador. But I felt proud, walking with bare head and bare legs. There wasn't any other girl like me there. In the narrow streets, on a hot, sunny afternoon of a public holiday, there was only the baking sun, dust, heat, sweat, and the smell of blood from the slaughter house, the only slaughter house in Tehran. The river stank and the dogs, lazy, sniffing, were everywhere. Men hung around on every corner like flies. I hate dogs. I hate their lazy bodies sniffing you.

In the railway, with every summer breath, the mixed stink of the river and the smell of blood and corpses filled my stomach. The air was sick and the heat spread the filth and dust around. I looked for a shadow under a bush, moved on, looking around the track for something worthy to take home. We came to a small mound of yellowish earth. We dug it with our sticks, and I unearthed some hard pieces of yellow clay. I took them and tried to write with them. I liked their fragile structure, their shapelessness, their softness. I felt a piece with my fingers – it was crumbling and left a soft yellow colour on my hand. It was easy and smooth to write with, unlike the white chalk I had at home, which was so hard, dry and stiff, and whose long, round, shape didn't crumble, but broke. I'd take them home and write with them, draw our hopscotch with them. I'd write things on walls with big letters and big words, like the writing we had seen. Chalks were very useful. I'd like to come back and get more of these when I ran out. I filled the pockets of my skirt with them.

It had been a very adventurous day for everyone. The boys had enjoyed playing with all the disused trains and Sara had loved climbing the trees, running across the tracks and poking about. I had some nice chalks and had seen the train tracks, stretching far into the distant clouds. I was puzzled how the trains could move on such narrow tracks. Sara couldn't answer my questions about it. Pity, I wouldn't be able to ask my father about it either. It was very odd that long trains, like snakes, could take so many people, as if filling up their stomachs; moving so fast, being so heavy, and all on such tiny tracks. How could it be? How far could they go? Where to?

We ran most of the way home, afraid of being caught and being beaten. My heart was beating in my chest like a trapped sparrow. Luckily, however, we weren't caught that day. We were safe. Pity that we couldn't tell anyone what we had seen – share our day's experiences.

Twelve

I was drawing on the ground, on the walls in our alley, trying out my yellow chalks. I was on my own, wasn't speaking to Sara. I had had an argument with her, she had pulled my hair and hit me. I had withdrawn in anger and hadn't given her any of my chalks. I wrote on their wall 'Sara is a donkey' three times. I wanted to write 'Sara is a bossy mule', but I didn't know how to write 'bossy mule'. I had only learned a few words, and those by just copying from others. So I left the writing on the wall unfinished and went to write on the ground. I enjoyed drawing there. I drew a large hopscotch. The yellowness made a nice effect on the black asphalt, the lines were thick and bits of the chalk were scattered on each square. The smooth yellow chalk finished faster than the hard, white one. I knew Sara would be envious. I decided I wouldn't give her any chalk until she apologised to me for beating me up.

I was writing the numbers on each square when I saw Shapor, Mother's half-brother, coming with his army clothes on, and his army bag hanging on his shoulder. He must be on leave today. I was happy, I went into the house. Mother welcomed him, she was glad to see him too. I asked my Daie (maternal uncle) whether he had time to teach me that day. He said yes, but later on, he must see his mother first and have a rest.

I asked my mother to give me paper and pencils. She said she didn't have any.

'Go and ask Shaba to give you some money to buy a notebook and pencils with.'

I approached Shaba gently and asked her in my sweetest voice to give me some money. Immediately she understood what I wanted it for, she burst out, 'No! I don't have any money for bloody paper and pencils! When you get hungry tonight you'll ask for bread, and we can't eat paper and pencils for dinner. Go and play.'

I turned to Mother disappointed and in tears. Mother got angry too, but said she didn't have any money.

'Shaba always keeps the housekeeping money and allocates it to what she thinks it should be spent on. I am not given the housekeeping nor any other money.'

I began to cry again, I was so disappointed. Shaba was mean, too careless of my needs. Mother saw me crying and unhappy, and scolded me for crying too easily and being so sensitive. She got angry and went to Shaba. Crying in despair, I could hear their arguments, as usual. Shaba blamed Mother for her young, fanciful, middle-class ideas; and Mother answered back that she was an old woman, illiterate, ignorant, and against change and education. She was dependent on her son, but her children would not be dependent on anybody, they would educate themselves to earn a living.

'Why do you hoard your money? Why don't you give a few pennies to Homa?'

'I have to save the few pennies I have to feed you all.'

'But she's not asking for much.'

'Paper and pencils are not a necessity, not for girls, anyway. Don't put your fancy ideas into her head.'

Mother was losing her patience.

71

'You're talking rubbish, "learning to write is a fanciful idea, a middle-class idea" . . . you are an ignorant old woman.'

'Yes, I may be, but what about you? Where has your cleverness and so-called education got you? Ha . . . what . . . a waste of time if you ask me . . . useless, you can't even cook.'

'You weren't blind, you knew I couldn't cook. You didn't give me a chance to learn.'

'Why did you get married then, my lady? You had the time to learn, you were twenty-five, perhaps you thought we would provide a maid for you, hmm? . . . Ha . . .'

'I had a maid in my father's house.'

'Don't boast so much. Shit on your education! Shit on your upbringing. As if your father's wealth was going to last you all your life. Thank God it hasn't . . .' Shaba didn't like Mother boasting. It hurt her very much.

'Shut up! Stop talking about my family. Stop insulting them! Shit on your family, ha!'

'You stop spoiling these kids, it's just like you to waste their lives with fancy ideas. Teach them something of practical use for their future.'

'Shut your mouth, you old peasant woman.'

It was a bitter argument, with bitter insults being thrown at each other. They usually argued like that. I hated it. I hated the argument and the hostility between them.

Daie heard me, came downstairs, and comforted me. 'Don't worry. I can give you a notebook and pencil.' I was so pleased, so happy to hear that. I dried my tears, stood up, cleaned my skirt, straightened myself out and got ready early to be taught by my Daie. I think he liked me, it was nice that he was so kind to me. I liked him. He was also a funny man and he told us funny jokes. Mother liked him very much too. Perhaps because he was a younger brother, and Mother didn't have a sister or brother of her own. She was an only child.

We sat on the stairs. The early afternoon sun was hot but kind and we were sheltered by the wall's shade. He still had his army clothes on. I liked his uniform, its green colour, its shining buttons and well-pressed coat and trousers. He had the coat loose on his shoulders, and only a T-shirt on underneath. He was young and handsome, the bronze buttons on his short coat shining and reflecting the sun.

'Open your notebook and hold the pencil like this . . . can you hold a pencil?' I was sitting one stair below him. He was much bigger than me and I had to look up at him.

'Yes, I know how to hold a pencil, my mother taught me.'

'Good. You're lucky. So I'll teach you to write your name and the alphabet today. How many letters have we got?'

'I don't know . . .'

'So you haven't been taught the alphabet yet?'

'No, but she showed me how to write my name.'

'Write your name then . . . that's clumsy, hold the pencil like this . . . in the middle . . . H . . . O . . . M . . . A.' I tried again. 'Join the letters together tidily, above the line. We have thirty-three letters. I won't teach you all of them individually, but through some words in a short sentence, like the ones you have in school books. The first-year school books start with two words, BREAD and WATER. I will write them for you. BREAD, WATER, each on a separate line. You must copy it five times on to each line. Look how I have written mine neat and tidy. Copy them exactly. Go on.'

I was writing. Hamid was poking a stick in the water and chasing the goldfish. Daie told him off. 'Don't do that, leave the poor fish alone. Haven't you got anything better to do?'

'He's very naughty, he does that all the time,' I complained to Daie.

'He is a pest, just like his father,' Daie protested, annoyed with him.

Hamid looked unhappy at being told off. He left the yard and went inside the sitting room.

I tried writing. It was difficult holding the pencil and keeping the paper still, but I tried very hard. I had to move around a few times, change my sitting position on the stairs and move the paper with me to feel comfortable. Daie wasn't happy with my clumsy attempt, but I tried very hard to write well and beautifully to please him.

'The second page of this book uses the words BREAD and WATER in two sentences. I'll write them down for you, and you must write ten lines of each. Look, like this . . . FATHER BRINGS IN THE BREAD. MOTHER GIVES THE WATER. Just as I write them, you must copy them. Copy them nicely.'

'Yes, I will, I'll do my homework.'

'Well, you'll be going to school soon, won't you?'

'Yes, I will, I hope so.'

'You'll learn everything in school, everything you need to know. The right things, the proper way . . . How much longer? Just another month and you'll be a schoolgirl,' he told me confidently.

73

'Yes, I will, I will!' I replied joyfully.

I was happy. I took my notebook and the pencil and went to my quiet corner, between the bundled mattresses and the wall. I wanted to be alone, away from everybody, and write my home-work. I'd write it more than ten times, yes, more; one hundred times, I told myself. The more I wrote and the better I copied, the faster and better I would learn.

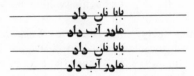

FATHER BRINGS IN THE BREAD.
MOTHER GIVES THE WATER.
FATHER BRINGS IN THE BREAD.
MOTHER GIVES THE WATER.
FATHER BRINGS IN THE BREAD.

I wrote on. And on.

Later in the afternoon, I tried to please Shaba and talk to her. She was still angry with me because I had created that argument between her and Mother. She was grumbling under her breath that she was seeing an unfortunate, godless future for me, and that she was worried for me, that she should pray to save me and my soul.

She went to the toilet and came back furious, slamming the door shut and shouting at me and Mother, 'Your bloody brother has pissed and wet all over the toilet. I hate him and his dirty habits. He stands up and waves his bloody prick, splashing all over the toilet. Why can't he fucking sit down like us women? Why can't he hold his prick and control where he pisses, right in the middle, not all over the place? Fucking men with their bloody pricks, they only know how to stick them up. We sit down in a civilised way and clean ourselves afterwards, so why can't they? I'm sick of men.'

Shaba always criticised this habit of pissing, but Father never took any notice of her. She was more angry with Shapor because he was Mother's brother, because he had higher status, and because he was teaching me.

Thirteen

Father wanted a party for his friends, and he reminded Shaba every day that the following Friday he had invited his friends to dinner, and that she must prepare the food carefully and make sure everything was respectable. This was because the meeting was very important to him. Shaba was not so happy about it. She complained that we couldn't afford to have dinner parties, to feed other people when we were hungry most of the time ourselves, and that it was too much work for her, the cooking involved for so many people. But she could never say no to him, so when the time got nearer, although she grumbled about it, she was resigned to doing it. Mother didn't bother to protest, but she didn't like his friends. She said it was a waste of money to feed those men.

Father came in with a chicken in his hand: it was pay day. He tethered one leg of the chicken to the water pump. It was a big bird with white and reddish feathers. Father said it would stay there till morning, before he took it to the butcher. I sat close to it and tried to pat its little red head. It was frightened and wanted to escape but it could only run in small circles, with one leg in the air. Looking at the angry bird I thought, 'Shall I undo the string and free it?' I sat there and thought about what it would do after it was free. But I didn't dare to.

Friday was a very good day. We had milk for breakfast. Mother took some money from Father and a bowl and went to the shop to buy the bread and milk. If Father had lots of money he would ask Mother to buy some butter and honey too. This didn't happen very often. Mother liked bread and butter and honey for breakfast, but Shaba and Father preferred milk.

Mother came back with hot fresh bread and a bowl of milk. Shaba put the milk to boil and then after she had placed it in the middle of the sofreh, we added pieces of bread and sugar to it, and soaked it. When it was cool, we all started eating from it. The milky breakfast was very tasty, much better than the sweet tea and bread that we usually had. I particularly liked it with lots of sugar if I could get extra, Shaba was very mean with it, and didn't let me have nearly as much as I wanted.

This Friday's milky breakfast was delicious and passed peacefully. But sometimes it didn't; the nights when Father had been out drinking, he usually had a hangover in the morning. He would be difficult and treat everybody badly. Then there would be long, nasty arguments between him and Mother. On such a Friday morning the milky breakfast wouldn't make any difference.

After breakfast, Shaba and Mother started preparing things for the dinner. Although they didn't like the extra chores, it was the only time that we could eat a decent meal, so they did it willingly. Father put on his trousers and got ready to take the chicken to the butcher to kill it. Hamid was going with him, but he didn't want to take me. He said I should stay and help Shaba. I got annoyed and insisted that I wanted to go with him and the chicken. Shaba said she could do without my help and that he should take me, so I tagged along. Father held Hamid with one hand, and the chicken's legs with the other, so that it should not escape.

Our local butcher had on a bloody apron as usual. His hands were red with blood and he was holding a large, sharp knife. Around us in the shop long pieces of lamb and cow, some of them whole, were hanging upside down. After they had exchanged long greetings, Father gave him the chicken and asked him to cut the head off. The big, fat, bloody butcher put the chicken's legs under his feet close to the drain on the floor, held its head up, and coolly slit its throat with a small, sharp knife. The blood gushed out and poured down through the drain; he held it there for a few minutes, letting all the blood drain out. Hamid was sitting close by and looking at it. I turned away and felt very sorry for the poor bird. The butcher let the chicken free, and it flapped on the floor, to and fro, resisting death till the last minute when it dropped dead, and its feathers drooped down. 'Don't be sad,' the butcher told me. 'Be strong . . . this is Halal now, the correct Muslim tradition of slaughter.' Hamid insisted that he wanted to carry the chicken home. I told him he was hard and heartless, how could he? Hamid said he was strong and wasn't afraid of it. The chicken's head was hanging down on a very tiny piece of skin. Hamid was proud carrying it home and showing off to the neighbours. Walking home I was sad, but when I saw the neighbours were having a good look, I smiled and felt proud too.

Mother had done the shopping. She had bought fresh vegetables, yoghurt, walnuts, pomegranate juice, rice and cooking oil. Shaba had brought the cooker inside the living room although the weather was still scorching hot. She didn't want to be in the yard when the men came. Mother had Vida at her feet and was cleaning the vegetables inside the room. Shaba had boiled a big pot of water and she put the chicken in it. She then took it to the yard, and, squatting by the hoze, well wrapped in her chador, she began plucking the chicken's feathers.

Father unlocked the door of the guest room and went in to check if everything was neat and presentable inside. He asked Mother if she had swept and dusted it. She said she had done all that yesterday. He took his newspaper and went into the guest room, and sat himself down there to read it, waiting for his friends to come. Hamid ran out to play in the street. I sat beside Shaba to help her.

I wanted to collect the feathers to play with them, but Shaba told me off. She said she wanted to keep them, to wash and dry them and collect enough to make a cushion or pillow for us later on. I asked her who was coming to dinner. She said they were Father's friends and she didn't know them.

'What are you cooking?'

'Fesenjan,' she told me.

'Oh, is it that tasty dish with walnut crunched up with chicken and pomegranate juice? I love it. But it will take a long time to crush the walnuts.'

'Yes, it will, but I'll do it after I have cleaned the chicken and put it on to boil.'

'I love fesenjan. It's so tasty. I wish you would cook more tasty dishes like this.' I was so excited.

'It's so much bother cooking for guests . . . all these men . . . they should go out and eat rather than bother us. I feel so nervous in case something goes wrong and it doesn't come out perfect. Your father will scold me, I'll feel embarrassed in front of the guests. I don't like it . . . really, if something goes wrong, he will kill me.'

'But you've never cooked anything tasteless, everybody knows that. I like guests, people visiting us. It's a change, and it's good fun.'

Mother called me in to go and look after Vida, who had just started crying. I took her away and tried to play with her. Mother wasn't happy, she was grumbling about the dirt in the vegetables, the heat, the amount of cooking she had to do, and wasn't sure she could have the dinner ready in three hours, by midday.

I was very impatient and looking forward to this tasty lunch. But it took Mother and Shaba a long time to prepare it. The chicken was boiling for hours on the single cooker inside the living room. Shaba was hot and sweaty under her veil, especially as the midday heat increased. She was crushing the kilo of walnuts in a pestle and mortar, and she went on and on pounding. It took a long time to mash it up. She got tired every now and then, changed hands, and swore at my father, calling him to come and help. But he didn't, and she went on mashing it, sweating, wet and tired, till it was soft and ready to be added to the chicken. Mother prepared the side dishes, yoghurt and cucumber, fresh vegetables, and she cleaned the rice. She set the sofreh ready and took out the much treasured china dishes hidden in her trunk, dusted them, polished them, and put them in a safe corner.

There was a knock at the door. Father put his newspaper away and went to open it. Mother and Shaba ran to the living room and hid there. Three men in clean suits, all shaven with shiny faces, walked in cheerfully and shook hands with Father. I watched them till they were inside the sitting room and sitting round the sofreh. Amo Salim came in a few minutes later. He went to the living room and greeted Mother and Shaba first, before entering the guest room to join the others.

When lunch-time was near, Mother put on her chador to go and buy fresh bread. Again she was grumbling about all those men sitting around in there talking when she had to go out to the shops. 'The least he could do is buy the bread for his guests.' Mother always grumbled.

Everything was ready for lunch to be served. Shaba was ladling it out of the pots and putting it in large china dishes in the living room, before taking it through to the guest room. The men were being served first. I was impatient to eat this delicious food as soon as possible. The smell was already making my mouth water so much that I thought my stomach would be full of water and there wouldn't be any room left for the fesenjan. I walked out of the room, and peeped into the guest room from the corner of the door. It was open and I was too shy to go in, but Hamid was already in there, sitting on Father's lap. They were sitting around the clean, white sofreh, and talking. I wanted to go in and pull Hamid's ears and drag him out. He went everywhere, he wasn't shy, he was rude and he wasn't being told off. Father's voice was louder. I leaned and squeezed myself against the brick wall, so that they would not see me. I listened to them and what they were saying.

'The factory is our base, we can strengthen our position and encourage other workers to join us,' Father was saying enthusiastically.

78

'But how? Surely we must be careful . . . now it is becoming dangerous.'

'Yes, but the workers are there, we need them.'

'But we mustn't distribute the leaflets in the factory. Talk to them, but distribute the leaflets outside.'

'I also think we shouldn't have meetings in our lunch break or make contacts then. The foreman is already watching us closely.'

Father's voice rose again, 'We can't meet anywhere else yet, we have no safer room anywhere else. Perhaps we should make the meetings brief and put the leaflets in the workers' lockers clandestinely.'

Amo Salim's voice slowly said, 'You're fools . . . what about the Party Headquarters or the newspaper office?'

'We can't. How can they trust everybody? We're still a banned organisation, don't forget,' Father protested to Amo's suggestion.

'Homa, come and take this food in, don't dither about there,' Shaba yelled at me. She had dished lunch out nicely in separate dishes. The black fesenjan in the white shiny china plates with red roses on the edges looked good and tasty. These china dishes, which belonged to Mother, were very precious to her. She had brought them from her parents' house. They were only taken out when we had guests – we never ate out of them ourselves. Mother took two platefuls of food in, while I carried the yoghurt dish. The men stopped their talk and said 'salam' to her. She tightened her chador and covered her face, bent her head and exchanged a few greetings with the men, put the dishes in the middle of the sofreh and went out. I did the same, but gave a bad look to Hamid who was still on Father's lap. 'Naughty, bully boy,' I grumbled.

'Why was he in the guest room?' I asked Mother.

'Go on, take the food in, don't argue,' she said.

'It's not fair, not fair at all. He always sits on somebody's lap and tries to make himself sweet. If I catch him I'll pull his stupid ears.'

After we had taken rice, tadic (the fried brown rice from the bottom of the pan) and the rest of their food to them and served them one by one, we sat down at our small, modest sofreh to eat the food in our usual enamel plates. I loved the food and asked for more, seconds and thirds. Shaba liked it so much that she ate with her fingers. Mother and Shaba had their seconds and thirds. Mother said, 'It is only because of his guests that we eat a nice meal . . . They've got aragh there too.'

'Well . . . that bloody impure drink . . . they can't do without it. They are men and they will never change, anyway.'

I ate the chicken meat and licked the bones and sucked the insides. It was lovely. I only stopped eating when I couldn't put another mouthful in. I left the room and went to peep into the guest room. The men were still eating, the food was nearly finished and the bottle of drink near its end. Father's voice was heard again.

'Mosadegh has again refused a united front against the imperialists with our party.'

'He hasn't changed a bit since . . .'

'He is as anti-communist as anti-imperialist, . . . a real bourgeois . . . his downfall will be in this too. He can't be more anti-communist than the British.'

'Herzhe Tudeh has opposed him for too long.'

'Still, with all his popularity and the mass support he has, he doesn't have a party, a strong central organisation to . . .'

'He has preferred to keep his political movement in a very traditional mass form, a combination of many different nationalist organisations rather than one central party.'

'And look how many of his friends have so far left him, joined his enemies, plotted against him. He is too naive a politician. He trusts the good heart of his citizens and their common sense too far.'

'His citizens have a good heart, fine, but with an empty belly a good heart will stop working. This is the result of the British boycott against Iran . . . imposed by a *Labour* Party . . . just think what kind of socialists they are . . . squeezing Iranian workers so hard.'

'The Labour Party there is very feeble. Mind you, Mosadegh's policy of strengthening small home industries and businesses has been successful.'

'This is ridiculous. You can't save a country's economy with patchwork like that . . . It's like the peace movement, silly people, soft-headed . . . Can you believe it? at such a time as this they've gone around collecting two million signatures for world peace. Like Gandhiism, I bet Britain loves it.'

'Our first and foremost aim, in a situation like this, must be to build the party and turn this nationalist mood into an anti-imperialist revolution for the final goal of workers' government in Iran.'

'But one of the problems with our workers is that they support Mulla Kashani on the right, right of Mosadegh – and pray behind him in the mosque.'

'They are only a few.'

'What? A few? You must be sleeping. It's quite possible that people will turn back and support Mulla's reactionary policies against British and American imperialism, not for a workers' government but for an Islamic state.'

'No, workers are not religious. Not really.'

'Well, they can be . . . if it happens I know where I will be. An imperialist state is more progressive than a medieval Islamic state. I prefer to go forward not backward.'

'Look, that's a wrong argument to follow. It's irrelevant. Everywhere in the world the people's struggle for socialism is going on. Look at Indonesia's communist party – it's the fastest growing and the largest and the best organised in the East . . . Even in Britain 4,000 dock workers are on strike in Hull . . . and . . .'

'Perhaps for a few more pennies in their wage packet.'

'. . . And there is a revolt in Chile, and Korea . . .'

'But along with all these struggles the imperialists are getting cleverer too and are using more subtle forms of oppression against the Third World. For example, Lord Mountbatten is in Turkey now, cruising around Cyprus. I wonder what he's cooking up?'

'Everywhere, even women workers are now organising strikes and pressing for unionisation.'

'Oh . . . women. Yes . . . women workers have arisen too.'

'We are the best organised party in this country, still underground but we have 2500 members and 400 000 trade union affiliates. And most important is our Army Officers Unit. It is small, but strong we will take over the leadership.'

'I'm doubtful . . . The way forward is strewn with problems. History is the recurrence of tragedies.'

Amo said the last word and silence fell.

I was leaning on the wall, watching Mother moving in and out of the guest room bringing out the dirty dishes and the left-overs. The men were full and had had enough to drink too. Shaba was getting ready by the hoze in the blazing heat of the afternoon to wash the numerous dirty dishes, plates, cups, spoons and forks all piled up around the big pots and pans. A huge square of dirty plates, gathered on the floor, surrounded her and she looked lost in the middle of it.

Father shouted, 'Mina, come and put down the mattresses.' She went in, put down the mattresses and clean sheets and prepared the pillows for the afternoon nap of the men.

Fourteen

One morning, I insisted on cooking and having some of my friends to visit, to play guests and hostess. Shaba promised to help me cook some rice and make some tea. Sara and I made a little sofreh just outside her house, put her little tea cups and dinner plates on it, and decorated it nicely. We were going to be the hostesses, and have Hamid and Sara's brothers as our guests. Shaba had cooked the rice in Sara's toy pan, and I brought it and put it on the sofreh.

We set out the plates properly, one here, one there: 'Clean this one; now, everything is ready, go and call for them.' Hamid and Hosein were ready.

'Knock, knock.'

'Who is it?'

'We have come to pay a visit.'

'Come in. Please sit down. How nice to see you! How are you?'

'We are well, thank you. It's so nice to see you.'

'How kind to come and pay a visit . . . we are glad.'

'Please, don't mention it, we are glad too.'

'Would you like to eat?'

'Please, don't bother.'

'It's no bother. We cooked especially for you.'

'Oh! We'd love to taste your cooking, it must be delicious.'

'Homa, give me a plate.'

I handed Sara a plate, she put some rice on it and gave it to Hamid, then put another one before Hosein and Hassan. They sat there, full of importance, backs straight upright, as they tasted the rice.

'Oh, it's delicious! You have some too.'

'Oh no, you eat first, we aren't hungry.'

'Oh, but you must, it's so tasty.'

Now all three of them were eating it up fast and handing us out compliments at the same time. After they had finished the rice, we served them tea. They drank and enjoyed it whilst we looked on, satisfied with our efforts. Hamid said, 'Thank you very much, that was very tasty, you are good cooks. We must go now.'

They stood up, thanked us, and went away. I looked inside the pan.

'The guests have gone now. Can we eat up the rest of the rice?'

'There isn't much left,' said Sara. 'We served it all to them.'

'Surely not all of it? I was looking forward to it. How stupid we are.'

'It's not my fault. That's what happens when you have guests round to eat!'

'But we were playing! I want to eat some rice . . .'

I began to moan and blame Sara for sharing it out unfairly. We ended up quarrelling and fighting over it, and parted in a bad mood.

Suddenly there was a shout from Sara's house. 'Sara! Sara! come quickly!' We both ran indoors. Her grandmother looked worried and agitated. 'Quick girls! quick! run up the road and call a taxi and ask them to wait until we are ready!'

Sara ran upstairs and saw her mother in the middle of the room, the other members of her family crowding round her. We both ran off down the alley till we reached the end of the third one, at the main road, and waited for a taxi to come. We stopped one and Sara asked:

'Will you please wait a few minutes till our patient comes?'

He nodded and waited a few seconds, then asked impatiently, 'What's wrong with your patient?'

'She has cut herself on a mirror and is bleeding,' Sara told him.

'Not another fucking abortion. I'm not getting my cab messed up with blood again,' the taxi driver shouted at us angrily, and he put his foot down on the accelerator and zoomed off, leaving us with our mouths hanging open.

From the bottom of the alley we could see Sara's mother being carried, her son on one side and my mother on the other, a small group of children following them. When they reached us they scolded Sara for being lazy and not getting a cab. Meanwhile her brother crossed over the road and went down the main road to try and get one. Sara's mother was leaning against the wall, her eyes half closed, her breathing coming slowly and heavily. Her face was as pale as a ghost's, and her untidy hair was swept over her face.

They finally got a taxi and went off to the hospital. Sara and I walked back home. Along our alley we saw drops of blood leading to their home, right up the stairs to the top room. Each step had a few red spots.

'What happened to your mother?' I asked.

'I don't know. Granny said she cut herself with a mirror.'

'Where did she cut herself? I didn't think a mirror could cut you.'

'I don't know. She was bleeding badly.'

'Yes, the taxi driver didn't want to get his cab dirty . . .'

'He was horrible, cruel . . . he wouldn't even wait for a sick person.'

'No, he wouldn't. He said something about an abortion. Do you know what that is?'

'Perhaps it's the word for cutting yourself with a mirror.'

'Did she cut her bottom?'

'Perhaps, maybe that's why they didn't tell us what was really going on.'

'How could she have the mirror near her bottom? What funny games your mother plays.'

'I don't know.'

'Shaba, do you know Sara's mother has gone to hospital?'

'Yes, your mother has gone with her.'

'Why did she cut herself with a mirror?'

'She was pregnant. She had a little baby in her belly, and she didn't want to have another one. Her son is a grown-up man, and she was embarrassed to have a full belly in front of him.'

'Why did she cut herself then?'

'Well, she didn't want a baby, so she pushed the baby out of her belly, then she had to go to hospital because she was bleeding a lot.'

'I don't like blood. It was everywhere, on the stairs . . .'

'Yes, it's cruel and dangerous. My cousin in our village died because she went too far and the blood didn't stop. The hospital was a long way away in the town, and there was no car to take her there.'

'Why did she do it? Didn't it hurt?'

'Yes, it does hurt, and it's a sin. God doesn't like it, and says women mustn't kill their babies.'

'Yes, I think it's cruel, poor little baby. I think Sara's mother is cruel. She killed a baby. I don't like it. Poor little baby.'

A few days later I saw Sara in our lane. I started talking to her about her mother.

'How is your mother?'

'She's all right now, she came back from the hospital yesterday.

84

The doctor said it was a boy.'

'Pity, you lost a baby brother.'

'I have enough of them. I don't want any more.'

'But I like babies, they're sweet.'

'I don't . . . they're messy and too much trouble, always fighting over the sofreh with my brothers . . . but I like your baby sister.'

'Yes, I like her too. She's very sweet. But still she is a lot of trouble you know, all that shitting and crying . . . but I like her . . . Shaba likes her too. I want to have children too.'

'Do you know . . . how babies are made?'

'Not really . . . But I know they live in Mum's belly and it isn't true that they come down the chimney, or that mothers buy them from the hospital.'

'I like children, but I don't like looking after them. They're helpless and slow and need help and attention all the time.'

'It's the same with me. I really only like playing with them when they're nice and clean and just fed; they smile all the time . . . I like that.'

'I like to dress them nicely and comb their hair . . . and put a nice pink ribbon in their hair.'

We were sitting and chatting casually at the end of our alley. We could see the boys playing in the wide part further away from us. I saw a big boy with his catapult putting some little stones in it, aiming at the small boys who were playing tileh bazi with their marbles. He was hitting them. The little boys protested, one of them starting to cry when a stone hit him in the face, but he still didn't stop aiming at them.

'Look at that bloody rough boy,' I said to Sara.

'I'm going to shout at him, the big bully,' said Sara. She stood up and went towards him. I was afraid for her. The little boys were trying to collect their marbles, and either wait for him to go away or leave themselves, so they could restart their game. Then I suddenly saw at the bottom of the wide lane a man who looked like my father, but his hand was in a sling, slowly walking towards me. Oh yes! It was my father! and in such a state, coming home so early! What had happened to him? I was scared. Oh God, I hoped he wouldn't see me out in the street. I dashed home like a rabbit running for its life. I ran into the sitting room shouting, 'Father is coming home! His hand is all bandaged up!' I dashed to my corner and hid there.

Mother and Shaba stopped what they were doing and looked at each other, panic-stricken. It was a bad sign, everybody was afraid.

What would happen to us now? I hoped he hadn't seen me in the street. 'My God, I beg you, I pray to you, I'll get up at four o'clock in the morning, please God, I will, and I'll pray to you every day if only he hasn't seen me. If only he doesn't beat me. Oh my God, I beg mercy, I'll be a good girl from now on. I'll do whatever you tell me to do . . . believe me . . . I'll do everything Shaba tells me to do . . . I'll pray all my life for you . . .' I was so scared, I was trembling and begging God not to let my father beat me up. Shaba was so frightened herself that she started reciting the Koran under her breath, and playing with her rosary, faster than ever. I waited there in dead silence.

He came in pale, weak, and in pain. Mother and Shaba started to prepare a corner of the room with soft cushions for him to sit on and lean against. Shaba was all apologies and regrets. She kept asking him what had happened, how he had got himself into that state. She started to make herb tea for him, and called Mother to prepare the ingredients. Both women started like two private nurses to provide everything for his comfort. I had never seen them so busy, moving around so fast, so caring and energetic towards someone. He told us that when he was operating his machine, which moves very fast, he had been tidying up a little screw that he had made earlier. In a matter of seconds he had lost his concentration and his finger had been caught in the machine and cut right through, nearly off his hand altogether. It seems his boss in the factory had called him up, and he was so afraid it might be for political reasons that, instead of finishing the screw and turning off the machine before going up to see him, he had cut his finger. It was very bad, blood pouring everywhere, and he had had to be taken to hospital.

He was still worried about what the boss had wanted to see him for. He was hoping to go back to work the next day to find out. Shaba got mad and said he couldn't go back to work in that state. He replied that he wouldn't be paid any wages for resting at home . . . and compensation . . . well, that was out of the question; the boss would accuse him of negligence, and the damage caused to the machine by him.

'Why do you think we go on strike and demand sickness benefit, and two weeks' annual holiday? Eight hours' work a day, and what for? For things like this. And you always say . . . go and work hard.' This was Father's answer to Shaba, who told him he must rest a few days at home, and that his boss was godless, cruel and mad if he couldn't pay his wages.

When I was sure that Father hadn't seen me in the street, I came out of my hiding corner and went and asked him what I could do for him. Could I get him some water? Could I get him some wet cloths? Some cold ice? Anything at all? He lay back on the soft cushions, and I and Mother and Shaba ran about attending to him. We were all trying in different ways to console him, care for him, and make him feel better. Three women were standing by his bedside, feeling sad and miserable for what had happened to him, and doing their best to make it easier for him. Shaba was so concerned that she kept praying for him under her breath all the time, and begging God to make him better as soon as possible. She looked sick with unhappiness; as if the awful accident had happened to her.

Mother wasn't as concerned as Shaba. She went on providing for his needs, waiting around by his bedside, taking his and Shaba's orders, and carrying them out. But she didn't look as sad as Shaba. Later on, when I saw her on her own in the yard pumping water, she was grumbling under her breath to herself that whenever *she* was ill, or had accidents like that in the kitchen, cutting the meat or chopping the vegetables, nobody was there to care for her, or give her attention. She had to bandage her cut fingers and begin the job again, and finish it, without any help. If she didn't, she would be blamed for it, or even worse, someone would have to go hungry or starve.

Fifteen

One dark night Mother packed a little bundle, took some soap, and whispered to Shaba. Shaba answered her loudly, 'All right, but take Homa with you for safety in case Eby finds out that you went out alone.'

'Come on then,' Mother called out to me.

'But where?' I asked, puzzled to be going out this time of the night.

'Come on, don't ask questions.'

I set off with my mother. Our narrow alleys had no light. We had to rely on the moon to lighten the passage of the night. I clung on to the back of her chador and followed her. She covered her face tighter and carried the bundle hidden under her black veil. We passed the narrow alleys and came to the main road. It was quiet, a few men were walking far away. We walked up to the top of the road. 'We must find somewhere quiet further from our house.' Just before we came to the end of the main road Mother stopped, looked around – there wasn't anybody in sight. Darkness hid people and the buildings in the distance. The place where we had stopped was clear and empty. 'I think it's safe here,' Mother said. She was standing by the gutter. It was wide and deep, and a narrow stream was flowing in it. The water was cleaner than in the daytime. I sat on the edge and took off my plastic sandals and tried to reach the water with my bare feet. Mother took out a long folded cloth to wash. I looked at it: it had a red patch in the middle. She took the soap out and bent down in the water to wash it. 'Get your feet out, you'll make them dirty,' Mother told me. I thought the water was clean, but still I pulled my feet out and put my sandals on again. In a while the water mixed with soap and blood and became red and lathery as it went down the stream.

'What are you washing?' I asked Mother as I saw the bloody water go down the stream.

'Just some dirty clothes.'

'But what are they, why are they bloody?'

'Well . . . nothing . . . they're dirty.'

'So much blood, where does it come from?'

'My nose was bleeding last night.'

'It's a lot of blood . . . why does your nose bleed so much? Did Father punch you in the nose?' I was worried for her.

'No . . . it isn't that. Go on and play, I will finish soon and then we can go home.'

A man appeared, walking down the way we were sitting. Mother saw him, immediately spread her chador and covered the soap and the clothes, and stopped washing. It looked like a big blanket covering her and everything else that she was doing.

She was motionless, totally hidden till the man passed. Then she relaxed, loosened the chador around her face a bit and continued washing. Why should we come out at night to wash in this gutter, and so secretively? I wanted to ask Mother, but I didn't. She sometimes didn't answer my questions, or said something totally different instead. I went away to play.

I found a stick and began poking it into the dark earth, digging and making holes nearby. The sky was lighter than the earth, perhaps because of the moon and the stars which were scattered around, spots of light peeping out of the sky. In the distance

Mother, wrapped in the black chador, squatting by the gutter and bending to wash the dirty bloody clothes, looked like a shapeless lump moving to and fro; like a huge snail in the darkness searching for food around herself. Shaba does the same when she is making dough, I thought. She squats and bends down (though not so far), and moves to and fro to turn the lump over and over. With slow movements she flattens it, squashes and rounds if off into a big lump. Again and again she beats it down and flattens it and rounds it up into a dough.

When she had finished we set off homewards. I was dragging my stick with me and kept looking back to see if it made a line on the ground. But I couldn't see much, though the moon was behind us, and I saw it following us.

'Mum, look at the moon, isn't it beautiful?'

She took a tired glance at it. 'Yes . . . it is.'

'Why is it following us? Look, it's been with us all the way.'

'The moon doesn't move, we are moving.'

'But when we turned the corner of the road into this alley, it turned with us behind us.'

'Really . . . well, it likes us, perhaps it's protecting us.'

I was looking at the moon: it looked like its picture in the books, it even had eyebrows and a mouth, and was still following us home.

In the morning after our breakfast, Mother asked Shaba for some money to go to the public bath, for her monthly ritual bath. This was usually a collective family bathing time. But Shaba said, 'It's too hot for me and my heart couldn't take it. I must go very early in the morning at four or five o'clock when the bath is cool and the sun isn't out yet.' So Mother packed our clean clothes and towel, soap and flannel, a kiseh (a flannel made out of rough material), and a packed lunch of bread and cheese. We all got ready to go, each carrying a little bundle under our arm. Shaba called after us, 'Don't stay there all day, come back before midday.' Mother told her not to worry, we wouldn't be late.

The women's public bath was in the main road. It had only one private bath, which could take one family at a time. But we always went to the public bath. The building was divided into two large rooms: one was the changing room, the other the washing room. The entrance door was always open and only a loose cotton curtain separated the changing room from the street. We went under the pale red curtain, crossed the threshold and climbed up into the changing room. Once there we left our bundles and sat down to undress. The middle-aged woman who ran the bath was sitting by the till.

The room was a carpeted platform raised above the ground, with a square hoze in the middle. The hoze had cool clean water running into it through a small fountain in the middle. There were many small fitted cabinets around the room for us to put our clothes in before going into the washroom. Some other women were taking their clothes off but it wasn't crowded. We were not supposed to look at women when they were taking their clothes off or when they were nude, but I liked to look at them. I kept my head down but shifted it to one side and looked at the women's bodies from out of the corner of my eyes, so that I wouldn't be noticed. If suddenly somebody's eyes caught mine, then I pretended that I was watching something else in that direction. Some naked women usually sat around the hoze. They were either the washer women, holding their kiseh, or women who had just come out of the bath and were cooling themselves down before putting their clothes on. Each woman had her hand over her private parts, covering them tightly, as if they were about to run away.

Mother packed our dirty clothes all together and put them separately from our clean clothes and towels in the cabinet, closed and locked it. We went along a narrow passage, through an iron door, and crossed into the washing room. The ground was wet and slippery, the room hot and steamy. The ceiling dripped with single drops every now and then. Many women and children were sitting around the hot-water hoze, which was in the middle of the room. Mother found us a place beside it, as this was the most popular spot. This was because, when washing, we needed to take water continuously from the hoze to rinse ourselves with. We had a small copper bowl and Mother filled it from the hoze many times and poured it over us while washing our hair and our bodies. Mother usually washed us first and then herself. Some women could afford to have themselves washed by a washer woman.

The washer woman did her job thoroughly. She would first rub oil into a woman's skin and then with her kiseh she would pull the dirt off. I often saw how hard she laboured, especially if she was an old and small woman, as most of them were, washing a large heavy woman. Most washer women had done this job for years, but they would still be sweating all the time while long pieces of rolled dirt dropped from their client's body. This was a good massage for women's bodies, because they were washed vigorously, and all their limbs shaken and moved around. Mother didn't have a washer woman for herself, she couldn't afford it, although it only cost a few rials. And she said that she was still able to wash herself.

The women by the hoze would wash themselves hard, first soaping their hair, usually thick long black hair, a few times, rinsing thoroughly after each wash. After their hair was washed and rinsed and shone with cleanliness, they would rub their skin with the kiseh to remove the dirt. They usually asked another woman to do their back. When this was done, limb by limb, they would rinse their bodies and then wash all over again, this time with soap and soft flannel, and finally rinse again. This was the last part of the wash by the hoze. They would then go to one of the single showers at the side of the bath, shut the iron door and rinse thoroughly again under the shower, also doing a ritual wash, while reading a few 'Ayeh' lines from the Koran.

Having a bath was a long procedure and took a few hours, especially for women with a few children. But they would turn it into an enjoyable, happy occasion too. They would bring fruit – grapes, watermelon, or a cucumber – let them cool in the hoze and eat them with their sandwiches, chatting with other women about anything and everything. The conversation would range from the most recent event to the latest gossip, with a lot of general complaining. Mother said that in the old days women came to the public bath for a whole day. They used it for public meetings, and sometimes clandestine political meetings took place there too.

When it was a social occasion, they usually prepared for it a few days in advance. They made the nicest food and desserts and cakes for the occasion.

Women talked to each other about their husbands, their problems, other women, and joked or despaired about their unhappy marriages. Mother would say a quiet greeting to a few neighbours, but she wouldn't chat to them. She didn't talk with the women as women do, didn't talk about herself, her life, her problems. She didn't share their conversation. Perhaps she didn't know how to, or how to make friends with them. Perhaps she felt too ashamed to expose herself. Or too proud to complain, which would be to lower herself. Perhaps she feared the exposure, or their judgement. As a middle-class woman she was separate from them; and living their life hadn't helped either. Perhaps she felt let down by my father, and therefore let down by his class. They had failed her, by their attitudes and their way of life, and that was all that there was to it. Her silence was her protection and rejection of them. Therefore she preferred to bottle everything up inside her and only talk to herself. Although I didn't understand everything she felt, I knew that Mother was lonely, even in that crowd, among women who had the same problems, the same unhappy life, the same aggressive husbands. How could she cope with such a burden of loneliness and mistrust?

'Why have you got a love bite on your back?' the washer woman asked a client, while washing her back. 'He threw the copper bowl at me, the brute, and it nearly hit my face, if I hadn't turned fast,' she complained.

'Haven't you got high-heel shoes? Or don't you know how to use them? They're really effective, especially on a man's head.'

'Ah . . . no, sister, he is too big, for me anyway. I can't stand up to him.'

'Well . . . they usually are . . .'

'He has the temper of a dog, so impatient and heavy-handed . . .'

The conversation, which had started between two women, was turning into a group discussion.

'I hear our next-door neighbour moaning and crying every other night. Her husband hasn't got a kind word to say to her, all I hear is "Bitch, slut, you're a whore, where have you been today? How did you spend the housekeeping money?" '

It seemed that most of their fights were over the housekeeping money.

'He thinks she steals some for herself.' This was another woman sitting at the other side of the hoze.

'Have you ever met a nice, considerate, polite man? Show one to me and I'll give you my right hand . . . Well, I haven't got a husband to bully me, but my sons are as bad . . . honest to God.'

'My major problem is his drinking . . . if only I could do something . . . in such hard times, with poor wages and cuts in his overtime pay, he still wastes most of his wages on booze.'

'We can complain about them till the end of the world, so what, what can we do? I'm going to take the kids for a picnic to the Shah-Abdol-Aziz, for a day, away from the fights in our house, to have a pilgrimage and to clear my head too.'

'What else can one do . . . nothing much really . . . just grin and bear it, as the old saying goes,' the first woman said.

Mother listened to their talk and sometimes looked from one

speaker to the other. In the end she muttered faintly under her breath, 'Yes, what can you do, that's right.'

I saw Farideh and Farid with their mother and aunt in a corner. Young boys up to the age of seven were allowed in women's baths. If Farid were older or looked older they wouldn't have let him in. Sometimes women protested sarcastically, 'Bring his father in the next time.'

Mother was washing Hamid, she looked busy. I crept towards Farideh, as they were sitting in a corner away from other people and washing themselves. Mother, unlike Father, wasn't strict about my friends, and didn't mind me talking or playing with Farideh. She herself said 'salam' to them too. Farideh was playing with her flannel and soap.

'Have you been washed?' I asked her.

'Yes . . . You?'

'No, Mother hasn't washed me yet. It will be my turn after Hamid.'

'I cried when Mum washed my hair. I hate it, the soap always goes in my eyes. Does soap go into your eyes too?'

'Yes, it's such a nuisance, I hate it too, bloody soap.'

Farideh's long fair hair was straight; it hung over her shoulders, dripping. I liked her fair hair and white skin. I thought it was nicer than mine. I had a brown belly and brown chest, but she had a white chest and white belly. I liked her colour better.

We began splashing water at each other, playing with the soap and flannel, washing them in her copper bowl.

'Why don't you come to our alley to play?'

'My mother doesn't let me, she doesn't let me go far. You can come to our house to play, will you?'

'I don't know, perhaps I can.'

'Do you play with Shahin? She only lives opposite your house.'

'Sometimes.'

'Hey, shall I wash you, like the washer women?'

'Yes, go on.'

I soaped my flannel. 'I can wash your chest,' I told her. Mother called my name at the same time. I left Farideh as it was my turn to be washed. Mother began to wash my hair. However tightly I shut my eyes the soap always went in them and made me cry.

The washer woman was still massaging women and pulling the dirt off. She was doing a nice job, tiring, but good for the women who were being washed and massaged. She must have enjoyed it too, rubbing women's hands, their soft round breasts, fat warm bellies and huge legs. I would have liked that job too. I liked to wash my dolly, especially her belly. We had nearly finished our wash by the hoze. After we had done so, Mother took us to a shower room. Just before we got in I noticed some women squatting close together, in a corner with their backs to us. Some were putting henna on their hair, hands and feet, some were putting a herbal cream mixture on their pubic area to remove the hair. Some women were shaving. 'It's for the men, they like it clean and shaven, no obstacles: hair is dirty down there but graceful up on your head,' one day Shaba had grumbled.

The shower room was quite a small square. We all squeezed into it. Just outside the door there was a long tiny gutter that led the water from all the showers to the drain.

In the little dim shower room mother adjusted the water to warm, and took us under the running water one by one. She rinsed herself and us thoroughly and properly, every corner behind our ears, and under our arms. Our bottoms were rubbed and scrubbed.

We left the steamy hammam for the clear, cool changing room, and sat by the hoze to cool ourselves down, as we felt very hot. A few women were already there, some drying themselves on the platform, some sitting on the edge of the hoze, like us. Here the air was clearer and cooler. Two women who sat next to us were very fat; they must have had difficulty moving about. Mother loved that. She liked to be very fat, and complained that she was getting thin because of us. She said that when she was at her father's home she ate a lot of sweet things and didn't do any work, so she grew fat and beautiful. But I liked her body as it was. It wasn't really thin and flat as she said, but it had nice bumps. I held her breast sometimes, when she was in a good mood, once in a blue moon, and asked for milk. She would gently push me away and say, 'You're not a baby any more.' Sometimes I wanted to be a baby again. Mother's belly was fat, full of birth lines (she called them 'birth bruises') but it was round and warm. Especially when she put me between her legs to dry my hair and my body. Then I would touch her body. She had big firm legs; once she said that was because she had cycled a lot as a young girl. My father had immediately shouted at her, 'You were mad to cycle around the city just after the war and under the allied occupation!' Mother said, 'Well, I did it.' So she got her strong legs then.

Mother dressed us first, then herself. By now we were starving.

94

We opened our dry cheese sandwiches, but with the help of cold grapes, cooled under the fountain, it was a tasty lunch which washed our insides cool and relaxed us. I loved chilled fruit after a steamy hot bath. I was always thirsty and hungry after the bath.

Two women were joking and laughing together about a wedding party they had been to.

'I was in such a rush to get there that in the hairdresser's, the woman nearly plucked my eye out instead of my eyebrows.'

'Oh, my hairdresser is nice, she always does mine first. I'm an old customer you see.' But the next part of the conversation they whispered in each other's ear, so we couldn't hear, and they laughed again.

The woman by the till called out loudly to them, 'Mulla's wives were here yesterday. You know, the one with a child wife . . . The poor girl looks like a pigeon, tiny, small and frail. Her breasts looked like tiny apricots, not fully out yet.'

'He isn't ashamed of himself, not a bit . . .'

'What do you expect from men? They all do that when they have the money. They take a liking to a new hole to push their prick in.' Looking at us who were eagerly listening to this group discussion, she covered her mouth. 'Sorry there are children in here, it's not nice to talk about these matters in front of them.'

'Men . . . God . . . they don't even pass a dog. It's a shame really. If I had a daughter I wouldn't marry her to a mulla,' one woman said bitterly and angrily.

'They are all corrupt . . . all men . . . "What's wrong with your wife? Isn't she a good woman? You hardly see her face, she is so virtuous, hasn't she produced some lovely kids? What's wrong with her? Is she unhealthy? unfit?" I can't make them out, the bastards. Just greedy men, bloody creatures . . . they just want a new cunt, a young cunt.'

The till woman spat with disgust and anger.

. A woman came in and rinsed her hands and feet in the hoze, as was the custom after leaving the bath. She was middle-aged and her breasts hung down. She said, 'Have you heard the radio? There are demonstrations everywhere in the country and the people are winning for once.'

'Ah? . . . yes . . . I have heard them: sitting here every day I see things. Demonstrations have passed this road a few times last week. I think there will be a big change soon.'

'A new government, I hope.'

'I have seen them passing my house, too, mostly youngsters, men shouting and swearing, most of them bare-chested like dastehs in Moharam. But they were shouting anti-Shah slogans, screaming, "We want our oil." '

'All these street protests are for oil. You know they say the English have been pocketing our profit. Can't we have it ourselves?'

'I suppose the men want the oil cheaper. It would be better for us too,' one of the washer women quiet so far said. 'It is the fight between the rich and the poor . . . God knows who will win in the end . . . the rich have everything in this world, all the comfort, good health and luxuries, and they can even buy up places in heaven by feeding the poor and giving alms and buying up the local mulla.'

'This must change.'

'You're right,' the other washer woman agreed with her, nodding her head in approval. They were older women, their breasts hanging down on their bony chests as Shaba's did; they looked dried up of milk and youth.

The same woman who had broken the news said, 'The English have been having our oil cheap to run their factories for years. What Mosadegh is saying now is that we want to dig our oil ourselves, process it ourselves, ship it and sell it ourselves, and have the profit ourselves too. But England says that is illegal.'

'They must have some funny kind of law and order in those countries,' another woman, who was putting on her blouse, chipped in.

'You're right, Mosadegh is right too – all those men demonstrating are right too. What is it to us? Hey?'

'It concerns us. It is our country. We . . .'

'What? Men are supporting each other, men are quarrelling with each other. What does it do for us? One man goes, another comes in his place. Things may get better a little, but soon afterwards with a new government and the Shah out of the way, and things quiet, everything will be the same for us.'

'No, not all the men are bad.'

'Yes, I have seen some nice ones in fairy tales.' She was a young woman, who had come out of the bath, sat down by the hoze and was cooling herself. She went on, 'We are expected to cook the men's dinners and will be for ever after. How can nationalisation of oil make our lives better? Women will still be doing drudgery and more drudgery. Let the men – English, Americans, Iranians – fight among themselves, bang each others' heads together – the more they kill each other the better for us.'

'Ah, yes, absolutely, I could kiss you for what you just said,' Mother, who had been quiet so far and was only looking at the women speakers and listening to them, said calmly.

'I don't like this talk, we can change things.'

'Yes, right. But not men.' She sighed deeply as if it pained her just talking about it. 'We are all talking from hard experience. Come on, don't worry, have a bit of this watermelon and forget your sorrows. They're not worth bothering about, it won't get better by brooding over it; the world has been like this for us as long as it has existed. Perhaps one day we and only we,' tapping her chest, 'will change it.' Some women had already started munching their yellow watermelon pieces.

Mother lifted her head up every now and then, listened, but didn't answer. I wanted to say that I didn't like the mulla either. He was nasty to children, especially the girls. But I didn't say it. I didn't think adults cared much for children's views.

The afternoon sun was beating down. The heat had driven people off the road to their rooms. The streets were empty, even the birds and flies had run away from the heat. We walked home, sweating all over. As soon as we got inside we dived under the cool sheet of the mattress and dozed off into a heavy afternoon sleep.

Sixteen

Sara called me out. I saw her face and I was pleasantly surprised. She had cherries hanging from her ears, two joined pairs hanging on each ear, and pink geranium petals stuck to her cheeks.

'How nice,' I said.

'Don't I look beautiful?'

'You do.'

'They are nice ear-rings, you know, there are three or even four joined together.'

'Where did you get the pink petals? Can I try them?'

'Yes. Go on.' She handed them to me. I looked at them and touched them.

'They're nice. You look nice in them, but I would look silly.'

'No, go on, try them.' I made a half-hearted attempt to hang them on my ears, but I soon took them off and gave them back to her.

'Women use all kinds of different things.'

'Yes, my father doesn't like it.' Sara hung the cherries on top of her ears again and moved her head around. The cherries dangled as she posed.

'They're beautiful . . .' I said, wondering how she had thought of it in the first place. It wouldn't have crossed my mind. She was clever and tried anything. We hadn't eaten cherries this season yet. I didn't even know they had come into the market yet.

'I like their colours. Shining red and soft pink.'

'I like their shape, round, soft inside; let's eat them,' I said.

'This one is yours.' She gave me a pair. I separated one from the stem and put it in my mouth. Crimson, soft and juicy.

'They taste sweet too.' I kept the other one for a bit later, but Sara had already eaten hers.

'The pink petals stuck well,' I said.

'I just wetted them with spit and stuck them to my cheeks.'

'My father doesn't like women putting on make-up, or wearing pink or red.'

'Why not?'

'I don't know. He just says it's bad for women. Red is a bad colour for women.'

'Really? How silly. Yesterday Mother was sitting badly. I could see her pants, they were red in the middle. I've seen it many times before.'

'So have I.'

'She says it's a woman's sign. Is red a woman's sign?'

'But it's blood.'

'Do you know why women bleed?'

'No.'

'Squeeze these petals. Perhaps they bleed too.'

Sara pushed them together hard between her fingertips. The juice made them pink.

'Let's write with it.'

'Yes, on Mulla's wall.' This was next to Sara's house.

'Write, "Mulla is a donkey".'

The crooked scribblings in pink marked the wall.

'He hides children under his "aba".'

'No, I can't write that. It's too difficult. I can't spell long words.'

98

'You know in the hammam they were talking about his wives,' I told Sara.

'Homa, if you promise not to tell anyone I'll let you into a secret.'

'No, I won't. Tell me.'

'Promise.'

'Yes, I promise.'

'I saw Mulla the other night with his wife, through a tiny corner of their window which wasn't covered by the curtain.'

'What were they doing?'

'I couldn't see everything, I was so afraid in case they might see me. My heart was going "boom boom".'

'Was he naked?'

'No. Neither of them were naked, but I saw her uncovered legs were open, and Mulla was in the middle of them.'

'Oh . . . really . . . ooooh! . . . Go on.'

'Yes, he had stretched out his legs, he still had his surplice on, and was trying to push his willy into her. It was a long willy.'

'Did you see her? How did she look?'

'I didn't see all of her because Mulla had dumped himself on top of her. I just saw her tiny naked legs. She looked so small underneath him, her legs looked like pigeon legs . . .'

'Was it like when we play Doctors and Nurses? Like when we go under the blankets?'

'Yes . . . No. We joke and have lots of fun.'

'Was she crying?'

'I couldn't hear anything.'

Mother put her head out of the door and caught us scribbling on Mulla's wall.

'What on earth are you doing? Messing up people's walls? Stop that . . . you'll get into trouble if Mulla sees you.'

'We didn't do all this . . . we had just started . . .'

'Never mind that. Go and call Hamid to come and eat. It's lunch-time you know.'

I frowned and walked away to find Hamid in the middle of a pile of rubber wheels and dirt.

'Come on. Mum's calling us for dinner.'

'I'm playing a good game, I don't want to eat,' he protested. I grabbed his hand and pulled him along. Walking along, we noticed Sara's elder brother, Hosein, was coming up behind us, shouting and waving.

'What's happening?' I asked him.

He was carrying a kite, which was made out of old newspaper on a stick, and was waving it around in the air. He was chanting something unintelligible, and thrusting his kite and his fist forward.

'He is funny,' said Hamid.

'What's up?' I asked him.

'Men are walking and shouting in the street just like this,' he told me, waving his kite as he spoke.

'What are they shouting?'

'They're shouting and screaming. You can't tell what they're saying. Some of them have got banners and are carrying written papers . . . They scream "Oil" . . . "The Shah" . . . They want oil and swear at the Shah, and the English; something like that . . . and they keep on repeating it.'

'Are they all men?'

'No, young boys. I'm going to join them tomorrow.' We passed Papa. He was sitting on his stool and laughing at Hosein. His rotten black teeth were showing. They looked ugly.

Dinner was mashed potatoes with fried onions, which we ate with bread. I liked it, it was tasty, but Mother protested and said it was all starch and had no goodness in it. Shaba was indignant.

'It is a good dinner. Why aren't you satisfied?'

'Potato and onion!'

'Times are hard, there isn't much money. Thank God, the Provider, for it; otherwise you wouldn't even have this.'

'Thank God, thank God for bloody mashed potatoes . . . then thank God,' Mother mumbled under her breath.

'I like it. It's very tasty, better than bread and sweet tea,' I said, in reply to Mother's complaint. Why did Mother complain about everything? Why was she never satisfied, grumbling and challenging all the time? What *did* she like? Shaba patted me gently on the back and said:

'Don't learn this thanklessness from your mother, complaining about everything. Be satisfied with whatever God gives you. Life will be much better when you take it easy and when you are satisfied with what the Lord gives. Always be patient, God will sort things out for you. One day, things will be exactly as you want them to be.'

I swallowed my food and shook my head. Mother disliked this advice. I slid under the white sheet for the afternoon snooze. Outside, beyond the frame of the living-room door, the sun was scorching hot, as if the brazen bright orange colour wanted everybody down and dozing. I spread my arms and legs out on the tiny narrow mattress, and whispered to Shaba:

'Tell me a lovely fairy story so that I can sleep.'

'If you close your eyes, you'll soon be fast asleep,' she said encouragingly.

'No, I want a fairy tale; a nice long one which will send me into a long, deep sleep; isn't that what you want?'

'Yes. If you have a long one. Let me think . . . which tale? I can't think of any offhand. This is a Turkish song well known in Azerbaidzhan:

My girl is as precious as gold.
Boys don't know this,
Well, let them get lost!
Who is suitable for my girl?
Whoever has gold.
Bring the gold to me,
My girl's dowry is a village
Not till then will she be a bride.

'Do you like it?'

'Yes . . . yes . . .' I didn't know really.

'That was a short one. I will tell you something longer. A story . . . Yes . . . one of the epic stories of Dadeh Ghor Ghord.

'There was a man who was riding out on a journey. He met another man and they travelled together. Outside a village, the first man stopped and asked the other to look after his horse while he went for a quick visit to the village. When he came back he remounted his horse, and they set off again. The second man heard the noise of wailing and crying from the village, but he didn't dare ask his companion what it was. Presently, they came to another village. Again the horseman asked his companion to look after his horse while he went in for a quick visit. When he came back to mount his horse, the other man could hear again the sound of wailing and crying coming from the village. They set off again, and the second man thought to himself that he must find out what this man's job was in these villages. So when they stopped outside another one, and the horseman told him to look after his horse, he mounted it himself, and rode a little.

'He saw that the ground beneath him shrank, and people looked small like ants scurrying about, and he was in control of everything on the earth. He knew that the horseman was the Angel of Death, and that his job was to go and help dying men, to relieve them of

101

this life. That was why he heard all those people crying in the villages. When the two men set off again, he told the horseman he knew him, and what he had done in the villages. He asked the Angel of Death, "Now, how long will I live?" "Only another three days. But if you can find somebody to give you his or her life, you can live longer." The man became very sad, and went home unhappily, to tell his father what had happened. He asked his father a favour. His father agreed. The son took a long needle and pushed it through his father's foot. When it reached his knee he shouted, "No, I can't take any more, pull it out and put it in your own foot." The man went to his mother, disappointed, and asked for a favour too. She agreed. He took a long needle and pushed it through her foot, and when it got to her knee she shouted, "Ah no, take it out and put it in your own foot." The man then went to his wife and explained his problem to her. She agreed to have the needle put in her foot. He pushed the needle through her foot, it reached her knee and she didn't complain; the needle reached her belly, and she didn't complain; the needle reached her head, and still she didn't complain. The Angel of Death was very pleased and told the story to God. God was so pleased with the woman's tolerance and self-sacrifice that he decided to allow them both to live longer together till they were sixty years old.

'Well, that's the end of the story. What did you think of it?'

'I don't like the needle business. I didn't like her having a needle in her foot. That was cruel. He should have died in three days.'

'Oh dear, sweetie, don't worry. It's only a story.'

'But some stories are true, aren't they?'

'Yes, but not all of them. I will tell you a happy ending, a nice story next time.'

I didn't really like the story. We were quiet for a while. I wanted to ask her questions, but I didn't know where to begin.

'Shaba, what will I be when I grow up?'

'You will be a beautiful young girl.'

'What will I do with myself?'

'You will fall in love with a handsome, strong man, who will love you and marry you.'

'What is love?'

'You like a man so much that you will do everything to make him happy, bear him healthy children, and live in a nice house.'

'Do I have to get married?'

'Yes, it's exciting, you will have the best wedding party, the most glamorous wedding dress, a white gown with lace and flowers in

102

your hand. I didn't have any of this, but I'm quite sure you will have it.'

'That's beautiful, it will be better than mother's wedding dress.'

'Oh yes . . . much better. Hers was very simple too, like mine. But you will have the best. You will marry a rich man.'

My eyes were already closing, I couldn't ask any more questions. I was wrapt in a dream of white lace wedding gown, flowers and sweets, in a drowsy state of warm cosiness. I loved it. It was a long, deep, sweet sleep.

It was a soft day, hot and heavy even in the shadows. I was in Farideh's house playing. Her mother and aunt were washing by the hoze. They were always washing something together, one of them often only company for the other sister. In the yard, it was getting too hot to be comfortable. We climbed up the stairs and Farideh took me to their top-floor room, which was empty.

'There are lots of toys to play with in here,' she said. I looked around. There were some plastic toys, squashed and dirty, some cracked wooden boards, a broken cupboard and pieces of torn carpet. The floor was empty and dusty, dust and dirt were everywhere: the window sill was thick with muck. It looked like an attic full of junk. Their house was exactly like ours, a small detached brick house with two storeys, but it seemed that all of them lived in the one room downstairs, and left this room unused. Farideh grabbed a torn carpet, put it on the floor and placed some boards around it.

'I play here quite often,' she said to me. She wanted to make a little den but it all collapsed.

'Let's do it properly,' I suggested.

'Yes, I want to make a little room so we can play in it,' Farideh said, fiddling with the boards.

'Let's put this cupboard here on the edge of the carpet first.'

We moved the broken cupboard over and stood it on a brick and supported the wooden boards against its sides around the carpet, so that they looked like walls.

'This is our home, this is our cupboard, let's put some things in it,' I said, looking around. A loose hinge nearly fell off, knocking over the cupboard and the boards around it, when I tried to shut the door. Farideh had to hold it while I put the plastic toys, a broken cup, and a soft legless dolly inside the cupboard, then we carefully closed it. We sat cross-legged on the carpet and looked around.

'This is our little house, I like it,' I said.

'I like the walls, it's more private.'

'Yes, we can play in our home now.'

'What game? . . . Let's see . . . this is our home, we can play husband and wife.'

'But we haven't got a boy here.'

'Don't worry, I can be a boy.'

'You? A boy?' Farideh was surprised.

'Just a pretend, why not.'

'All right then.'

'I am your husband, you are my wife, like my mother and father, and this is our home.'

'I want to be the husband.'

'No, I'm bigger than you, and you're more beautiful than me.'

'OK, let's go to bed then.'

'Take off your pants.' I took mine off and we put them under our heads and lay down next to each other.

'Come closer, we can play like my parents.' She came nearer and soon we were stuck to each other tight.

'You haven't got a willy.'

'Yes, but that doesn't matter.'

'It does, men have a big willy and it hangs down,' Farideh persisted.

'Well . . . I can make one . . . a fine one.'

'What?'

'Yes, it's just something long. Let's look around and find something . . . What about this thing?' I found a round, thin piece of wood two inches long and showed it to her.

'How can this be a willy?'

'Look, I'll make it into one. You just put it between your legs and then you're a man.'

'How?'

Yes, how? . . . with a piece of string. I looked around, and among the junk and the muck in a corner I found a long piece of string. I held the wooden stick between my legs like a willy hanging and worked out how to tie it there. I cut the string in two and tied one end of each piece to the wooden willy, and the other end round the top of my thigh.

'Look, it looks like a willy, it wasn't difficult, open your legs.'

'It looks funny.'

'They all look funny, come closer.' I held the stick willy in my hand and tried to push it in between Farideh's legs.

104

'It won't go.'

'It hurts,' she exclaimed.

'Doesn't matter, it always hurts. Be patient, open your legs more.' I tried to push it inside her again, just like a man really doing it, but it wouldn't go.

'It hurts, I don't like it.'

'Be patient, it will be all right in the end,' I insisted.

'No, don't push it any more, it hurts, I'm afraid.' I stopped.

'You're impatient, my mother takes it, doesn't fuss like you. Perhaps it will be nice in the end.'

'No, it hurts me, I don't want to play such a painful game, take your bloody willy away.'

'All right, if you're so delicate. I'll throw it away, we can play another game instead.' I took the wooden willy off the string and it took me some time to untangle all the strings attached to me.

We sat and looked at each other.

'So what now?'

'We can play patient and nurse,' Farideh suggested.

'I'll be a nurse and you a patient, all right?'

'Yes . . . how? I . . .'

'I will examine you to see what's wrong with your body. Take off your clothes.' She took the soft cotton dress off herself, and so did I. My heart went boom boom. She lay down. She looked thin and pale. Her ribs were showing, her stomach was bulging and her chest was flat. I ran my hand down her stomach, chest, nipples. Her heart was ticking hard too.

'Your heart is beating hard, are you afraid?'

'Yes, but I like it. What if my mother comes in?'

'I like it too. But my stomach is turning inside out. How is your stomach?'

'Bad.'

'Let me rub it better.' I rubbed her belly gently. I moved my hand again.

'No, it's not good, stop it, my stomach is popping out,' she told me.

'Do you want to be the nurse, and I'll be the patient?' I asked her.

'Yes,' she said.

'Come then, touch me here. I have a big pain here.' I put her hand on the middle of my stomach. 'It's beating like my heart.'

'Shall I rub it for you?'

'Yes, please.' She moved her hands around my fat belly. I was dead scared in case somebody came in and saw us in that state. But I was enjoying it.

'Can I look inside your fanny?' Farideh whispered to me.

'Yes go on, . . . look for the treasure . . . we'll share it.'

That afternoon, with all those fears in our hearts and our minds, with our hearts beating and stomachs turning, we went on touching and kissing, rubbing our bodies together, sticking to each other tight. Every sound from downstairs made us jump. It was different this time with Farideh, not like the other times that we had played doctors and nurses games in ours or Sara's house. I really liked Farideh and liked to play with her.

If my father found me like this, I thought, he would beat me to death with his leather belt. He had told me to play with younger girls always, much younger than myself and never with Farideh, because younger girls can't teach you bad things.

Seventeen

Sometimes I went to the toilet and shut the door and stayed there for a long time. When I wanted some peace and a dark corner with a locked door, I would choose the loo, as there wasn't anywhere else that I could have to myself, even for a few minutes. It was difficult to sit there as there wasn't a seat. The toilet was a large oblong hole in the ground, and we squatted, one leg on either side of the hole.

I pulled down my pants and squatted, sitting there thinking. I could see a pile of shit, all different colours. It didn't bother me, but the smell sometimes cut through my thinking.

I repeated what Mother had said. 'If the big boys beat you up, it is your fault for going out to play.' Shaba's kind advice, Father's continuous reading of the newspapers and his comments on the Shah, the Prime Minister, the oil and communism. I didn't understand any of these things happening around me, nobody explained much about them, but I had memorised everything that they had said or done which was interesting to me, and I wanted to remember and know more about them.

Why is Mother so unhappy, so lonely and so dull? Why does she talk to herself? Even Sara makes fun of Mother and her talking to herself aloud when we are cross. She says my mother is crazy. Is anyone who talks to themselves crazy? Is it bad to talk to oneself? Perhaps she shouldn't do it out loud, then nobody would hear her, nobody would notice her, and nobody would say that she was a madwoman. I talk to myself, but I do it quietly, like thinking, so nobody can hear me. Perhaps because she is so busy looking after Vida, doing the housework, she doesn't notice other people around or what she is talking about. Perhaps she doesn't even care about them. This working too much, Vida's nappies and shit made her crazy in the first place. Caring so much for such a little one. Father doesn't like her either. He swears at her, calls her a bitch, slut, a cow (I like cows, they are very useful animals. What's so bad about a cow?). And my grandmother isn't nice to her either. They always argue, disagree and insult each other. Why? Shaba calls her a spoiled little rich girl who doesn't know how to cook and how to look after her husband. She calls her a bad wife, full of fancy ideas. So Mother isn't just a madwoman but a bitch, a bad wife, and a day-dreamer. All these things. What else? She beats me, she is unkind to me and never talks nicely to me or kisses me the way she does Vida, never gives me a penny or buys me sweets. It seems she has had enough of me, or doesn't care about me, or perhaps she doesn't have a heart?'

Shaba has a heart, a big one too. She likes me, spoils me, gives me sweets and pennies. I like her very much, I will always like her. I'm not sure if I like anybody else so much: Sara a bit, when she is my friend and sticks up for me. But Shaba doesn't want me to go to school. She wants me to stay at home all the time. That's very boring and there's no fun in it. She says it's better to get married young when you don't know much, when you haven't learned other things. It's not good to know too much, it makes you unhappy; good women stay at home, have no fun, and aren't educated, 'like your mother', she says. When you get married young, then you like your husband more and look after him and the children better and have fewer expectations and fanciful ideas. If you know other things, if you're educated, you'll be asking for too much and then you'll make yourself unhappy and everybody else unhappy too. You'll be bad-tempered all the time, argue with everybody and in the end want a divorce, like your mother, she says.

They don't want me to play outside the house. But I don't understand why not. It's fun. I like it. I enjoy playing outside the house with other girls on the see-saw or playing hopscotch. Why can't I do what makes me happy?

They're just like Mulla, who tells us off, who says to us, 'Don't play', 'Stay at home', 'Jumping is bad for girls'. Shaba says that girls have something like thin skin inside their fanny, they must look after it well. That is our treasure. Why is this treasure so precious that I cannot have fun? Perhaps Shaba wants me to marry a mulla? She would like that. She loves God and mullas and prays to them all the time. She says if I am a good wife I will go to heaven. I ask her what heaven is like and she says, 'There is every kind of good food and fruit, wine, beautiful young men and women in splendid gardens full of trees and colourful flowers, and an easy life.' I ask her, 'Why can't we have all that here, in our house? or on the earth while we are alive?' She says, 'No, that is a sin.' 'What is a sin?' 'It is very bad.' 'Why is it bad on the earth and good in heaven?' She says she doesn't know, God says so, that's it. Does she know God? She says 'No', but Mohamad our Prophet has seen God. Who is she? No, 'he', she says, he is a man, an important man. I don't like important men like Mulla or Haji. They frighten me. They have too much of a respectable air about them. Everybody stands up for them and greets them. I want to throw a stone at Mulla, pull his long flimsy robe.

The smell of shit reached my nose. I held my nose and breathed through my mouth to avoid it.

I don't understand all of Shaba's stories, but they are nice, like fairy tales, fantastic, except that Shaba really believes everything she tells me. I can't believe it. I hope she goes to heaven, she is so worried that she may go to hell. I don't like hell, and I want her to go to heaven. Perhaps I can help her when I grow up. She says if you pray more and more you go to heaven. When I grow up I can pray a lot and ask God to count it as hers.

Father says heaven is in the luxurious part north of Tehran, Shimran, where the rich people live. They all have good food and wine, beautiful colourful flowers and trees, and a very luxurious, cosy life. They have never suffered in their lives. Father is the hardest to understand. He reads the paper all the time, bosses everybody around to give him his socks, give him a glass of water, give him tea: and then all those big words on communism and the workers' government. Will I ever know what he's talking about? And what these things are? Why do they make them so difficult, these adults? . . . He must know a lot. He does . . . except when he recently asked Mother what ideology was. She said, 'It's like culture, tradition, religion.' They argued over it for a long time. He said no, it wasn't important, Mother said, 'Yes it is important'; and so they went on. What's the use of him knowing a lot when he's always too tired to explain to me or to anybody else what he's talking about? Perhaps that's because he works long hours. We only see him for an hour each day. Even then he doesn't have time to talk to us, he's too tired, too hungry, too dirty, too sleepy. Perhaps he doesn't like talking to me. He thinks that I'm a child, a girl child, and I don't need to know everything that he knows. Perhaps he doesn't care about me at all? Perhaps he thinks like Mulla, that girls shouldn't do this, shouldn't do that. But no . . . he doesn't think like that. He doesn't believe in God, he doesn't pray, he always 'fucks God' and makes Shaba angry by saying things like that. He hates the mullas. He says there are lots of them, the country is full of them. They rot people's brains. But they look so innocent and passive, always bending their heads: how can mullas rot people's brains? They aren't maggots, and people aren't apples. But he's right when he says they have lots of money, eat good food and have many women. He must be very rich, he's the only one in our area who has a talking machine. We sometimes stick our ears to their wall to hear their radio and they have it on very loud for everybody to hear.

They eat well too. I have seen sometimes when Mulla's door is open, his first wife is always cleaning a chicken or washing rice. They must be eating good food. He has a big belly like Haji. But even if I don't like Mulla himself I like the chador his wife wears and the way she wraps herself inside it. I'd like to have a chador. It must feel good when you wrap it around yourself. I can hide under it too. It would be good to play hide and seek under it so nobody could find you. Everybody would think you were a cushion and you could hide there for a long time. It's a sign of being a woman, a grown-up, not just a girl. I like cooking too. All the food preparation, and cooking it on the cooker and sitting by it and dreaming. But I don't want to be doing it all the time, only when I want to. Father says we can't afford to have a chador for me. But most women wear the chador, where do *they* get the money from? Perhaps their husbands buy one for them and I'll have to wait till I have a husband. But a husband is a father too, usually anyway.

I had reached a dead end . . . I couldn't understand some things around me . . .

I may not understand most of the things that my father does or says, his meetings, his drinking, his evenings out with his friends, but I know why he hits my mother. He wants everything to be done for him and when she doesn't do it he beats her up. I don't like that. Why shouldn't Mother refuse if she doesn't want to wash his socks and pants? I know that he works hard in the factory and that he is tired when he comes home. But why should he beat her up? He's just showing off his muscles to her. I think Mother should go away next time he attacks her. She shouldn't take it. If she goes, then Father won't have any clean clothes at all. But I think his mother will do it for him. She shouldn't. He's not nice towards his mother either, except that he hasn't beaten her up yet.

The world of the grown-ups is very complicated. How can children make sense of it? I don't know. Shaba says I will when I grow up, but when will I grow up? How? When? Where will I be?

Shaba knocked on the door and I realised that I had been there, still squatting on the toilet, wrapped up in my thoughts, for a long time.

'I'm coming out.'

'You've been there for ages, girl, has it stuck? Can't you push harder? Come out soon or I will be shitting myself.' I pulled my pants up, unlocked the door and let myself out.

'Get in now,' I told Shaba. 'What a hurry.'

Pushing harder doesn't always mean relief, but it can leave one pink-faced.

Eighteen

When we heard the chanting of the dasteh processions, and saw black flags on some of the houses, we knew that Moharam was here. Moharam is a holy month for Muslims, the anniversary of the deaths of some holy Imams. Mourning services were held in the mosques, and rozeh, or sermons, in private houses in the evenings. The processions, with people beating themselves with sticks and whips, usually began in the main road. When we heard men shouting the slogan, 'Hosein, I sacrifice myself for you, tonight is the mourning night for you,' we would rush into the street to watch them. Sometimes, especially on the night of Hosein's death – the seventh day of Moharam – the processions were very grand and ceremonious. Some men would carry elaborate banners which had candles and long feathers on the front. Young men followed behind them, beating their chests or shoulders with lashes of small chains. A group of women followed them with small children, all robed in black. They marched through our streets where local men joined them to go to the mosque. There they would sit in the yard and listen to the sermons, beating their breasts and crying out loud, long into the night.

I loved this dasteh, the sound of their chantings. I dashed to watch them with the other women who could not follow the procession. Sara's brothers always joined them and followed them to the mosque. Later on they would come back and tell us stories about the good food they had eaten, the many songs they had sung, and how some men had beaten themselves with the chains so much that they had had to go to hospital with their wounds. Haji, in our street, observed the Moharam ceremonies every year. He put a large black flag on top of his house, and held rozeh indoors, when Mulla would preach sermons and encourage people to whip themselves, and wail out loud. Most of the neighbours went to these evenings, but we couldn't. I enjoyed it, not because of the sermons, but because we could stay up till late, eat nice food and cakes, and play with our friends. We got up to tricks whilst our mothers were crying and lashing their chests.

This year, Moharam coincided with the hottest part of summer, the scorching heat in the middle of August. Women put on their blackest garments and covered their faces even tighter. My friends put on the chador. They looked pretty and I envied them, I wanted to have a chador too. I asked my grandmother.

'Shaba, I want a chador.'

'I haven't got one. I don't have the material to make you one.'

'I want one. All my friends have got one.'

'Ask your mother.'

'She doesn't want me to wear one.'

'Ask your father.'

'He wouldn't listen to me. Please can you ask him for me?'

'Well, I don't know, you know he has a foul temper.'

'He would listen to you. Just ask for some money to buy the material for me. Don't say it's for a chador.'

'All right, I'll try when he comes home tonight.'

I waited impatiently, and tried to be well behaved. In the living room I quietly played with my five-stones, and didn't say a word. I listened to Shaba, took my mother's orders, and looked after Vida.

Father came in in his greasy blue overalls, a newspaper crumpled in his hand, sweating, and angry as ever. He looked tired, dirty, and harassed. He sat down and immediately started talking while Mother was preparing his wash.

SHAH'S SISTER PREVENTED FROM RETURNING TO THE COUNTRY
DEMONSTRATORS DEMAND CONSTITUTIONAL ASSEMBLY

ELEVEN MEMBERS OF OUTLAWED GREEK COMMUNIST PARTY
SENTENCED TO DEATH

NEW OFFENSIVE SPREADS IN INDOCHINA AGAINST THE FRENCH
TRUCE SIGNED IN KOREA. WAR ENDS. THE COUNTRY IS DIVIDED.

'The British Navy are in the Persian Gulf,' he was saying to himself. 'They could invade us. The Americans are behind the British, the country is in chaos, it is divided, it can't defend itself.'

Shaba sent me messages with her eyes that it wasn't a good time to ask Father now, perhaps after dinner. I helped Father to finish his wash, gave him a soap and towel with his pyjamas, and waited around meekly.

Father and Shaba were drinking tea and musing after dinner. I was impatient, there was a pause, and then Shaba asked sweetly:

'Can you spare me some money this week?'

'Why? What do you want it for?'

'Just a few pence . . . something . . .'

'But you know money is scarce and wages are not paid on time. I'm still owed three weeks' overtime.'

'It won't cost much . . .'

'What won't?'

'Well, Homa fancies a chador, her friends are wearing them because of Moharam.'

'Oh, damn that. It's nothing to do with us. This fucking business of Moharam, mourning, and everybody turning into blackbirds . . .'

'There is a rozeh in Haji's house, her friends go, it's just a fancy, she wants to be like them.'

'We can't afford it. I haven't got the money for such extras.'

'It's not an extra. You make your wife wear one. It's good for her. It will teach her.'

'I have no money.'

'You have money to spend on your friends when you go out,' Shaba lowered her voice, 'when it comes to us, you're broke.'

'Woman!' he screamed. 'Soon there will be a civil war, the country has no government, and you stupid women are asking for more veils!'

112

'I don't care. Fuck the Government, let them sort out their own problems. It's their shit, let them eat it. You do your work, and don't go mixing with those troublemakers.'

'This is God's preaching for you!'

'Keep God out of it. Don't be blasphemous. If you and the likes of you had said your prayers and been responsible Muslims, we wouldn't have any of these bloody troubles now.'

'You can keep God. She is not going to a bloody stupid mosque, or rozeh, and neither are you.'

'You can tell your wife and daughter what to do, but not me. In my old age I won't obey you. I want to go out, see some people and listen to a sermon, like everyone else. Why can't we be like everyone else?'

'We can't. We are poor, we are workers, we are not like everyone else. Anyway, they are stupid, ignorant and illiterate. That is why Mulla and Haji can so easily lead them on.'

'If you ask me, it's you who are stupid and ignorant! You have forgotten the God that created you, His Prophet, and you have no respect for Imam Hosein's anniversary,' Shaba was moving away from him and getting angrier, 'and you think you are so fucking high and mighty! My God, what have I brought up? All my years of struggle to feed you . . . it's all my fault . . . I shouldn't have taken you to that godless country.'

Father hated Shaba to talk of the Soviet Union like that. He threw down his paper in a rage and waved his arms around in anger. I was afraid now, really afraid, and trembling. Would I be beaten? I slowly shifted backwards on my bottom towards the far corner of the room. I didn't want any arguments, I hated them. I didn't want the bloody chador any more.

'Woman, you just don't understand. You *cannot*. We're having a revolution and you want to go and cover yourself up in a black veil and hide in a dark corner in a rozeh or a damn mosque to cry for fucking Hosein's death which happened thirteen hundred years ago! Woman, you're barmy, do you hear me? Fucking crazy . . . I fuck your God, fuck that Mohamad you pray to. To hell with all of you who are so screwed up, you stupid cunts.'

Shaba was in the other corner of the room, tidying up the tea plates and moving around, spreading out the bedding. She was silent for a few minutes, but her movements were furious. She was grumbling under her breath incomprehensibly while she put down the mattress.

Mother was in the yard by the pond washing the dinner plates.

113

She was lingering. She didn't come in until the argument was over. Perhaps she knew what was happening, and didn't want to get involved. Why not? Why wouldn't she stick up for me? It seemed as if she didn't want me to wear a chador, it wasn't fair.

Father was under his blanket, Shaba was still grumbling under her breath.

'You, my son, damn you, we are sick of you and your prick trying to be the big boss . . . fucking everything and everybody, shame on you! It seems the only thing you can do is fuck.'

I went to bed with tears in my eyes, and cried myself to sleep. I hated my father's big ideas. He was just a bossy-boots. He didn't care about me and what I liked, he just wanted us to obey him. He was an ugly, angry bossy-boots; I hated his big talk.

Every day I kept close to Shaba and asked her to make me a chador, so one day she just agreed to tear up one of her own skirts and cut a chador out of it for me. I was head over heels with delight, but Shaba wasn't so happy to lose a skirt, she didn't have many anyway. She measured it to my height, cut it, and began to sew it by hand. It was all done in an afternoon. I couldn't wait to put it on and go out and show off to my friends. My friends liked my chador. They tried it on, and we decided to play Mummys and Daddys, and Guest and Host. We wrapped ourselves in it like our mothers did.

One night, after Father had changed, eaten, dressed and left for a meeting, I said to Shaba:

'Let's go to the rozeh in Haji's house.'

First of all she wouldn't; then she agreed to take me. She put on her chador, which, unlike other women's, was not black but made of soft white cotton patterned with small green dots. My chador was brown with large yellow and green leaves all over it. With one hand, I held my chador under my chin like my mother did, and with the other I clutched on to Shaba's chador and we walked through the long mosaic corridor of Haji's house to the women's section of the rozeh.

Their yard was grand and spacious, their hoze a big marble circle with a few fountains in the middle. The rozeh was at the top of the yard where a large area was divided into two, segregating men from women. A black curtain was fitted round both sections, and the area around it was covered with beautiful soft Persian carpets. We went into the women's section, taking off our shoes at the entrance, and sat down on a red and blue carpet. The space already had some women and children in it. The women had covered themselves so much that I could hardly recognise them, squatting around the edge

114

of the curtain in black chadors from which only their eyes peeped. I sat close to Shaba and it took me some time before I got used to the dim light. I looked around for friends. Shahin wasn't there, nor her mother. Perhaps they were in the kitchen preparing tea. Farideh and her mother were sitting in the corner. I gestured to her to come over and sit by me. She whispered to her mother and then slid over the carpet towards us.

'You've got a chador too!' I said

'Yes, my mother made it for me. Do you like it? I like mine very much. But sometimes it's a nuisance when I want to walk fast.'

'Shaba made mine for me, it's nice wearing it, isn't it?'

'Yes.'

Some women were reading verses under their breath and counting their rosaries. Shaba was also mumbling, 'Allah, Allah, God is great,' about twenty or thirty times, counting her beads, one by one. I think she had made a vow to God. Two women were sitting and reading the Koran. They looked as if they were showing off that they could read, but perhaps they were just looking at the book and mumbling. I could see that their hands, holding the book, were covered with gold jewellery. I nudged Shaba and whispered in her ear:

'Look at all that gold!'

'Be quiet,' she said, 'and don't stare at other people. Your mother had gold like that too, three times as much. Didn't you see it? Well, it's gone now.'

I told Farideh I thought the women looked like aubergines, the way they were all sitting wrapped up in black. She laughed, and told me to hush. We found a gap in the curtain and peeped through into the men's section. There were young men and old men sitting cross-legged on the edge of the carpet. Some of them wore black all over. There was a long, white sofreh in the middle, full of cakes, fruit, dates and nuts.

'Oh look!' I said. 'Why haven't we got any of that here?'

'Don't be greedy,' Farideh replied, 'They'll give us some after the men finish, we'll get the left-overs.'

The men were also mumbling and counting their beads with their heads bent. Most of them had clean white cotton shirts on with open necks and short sleeves. We could see their short hair, moustaches and beards, neatly cut as a sign of respect for this holy month.

The pulpit from which Mulla preached was in the men's section, but near our curtain so the women could hear him too. Farideh and I pointed to the men we knew and whispered to each other. They were our neighbours' brothers, and fathers of our friends. Some of them we didn't know.

'Look at that man's moustache. it's called a Genghis Khan moustache. That man is bald except for three hairs on the top of his head. Why do men get bald?'

'Because their heads are empty so they can't nourish any hair.'

'You mean my father's is too?'

'No, your father is different, it's because he works hard.'

'I like that man's eyes, so black and large.'

'Shut up, that's not nice.'

'Look at that man's ears, he looks like a donkey.'

We both burst out laughing and Shaba grabbed my shoulder and pulled me back in.

'Shut up, girls. Laughing in a rozeh, shame on you.'

We turned round and sat as quiet as two mice. More men were coming in. Soon Shahin came out of the kitchen, only her round face visible under her chador. We winked at her and she sat next to us. The three of us held hands and pretended to be sad and moaning whilst waiting for things to liven up a bit. I half turned and peeped through the curtain again. Mulla appeared in his long brown cloak and huge white round turban. Haji went to greet him, and they shook hands and smiled at each other. The men looked up as Mulla walked in, and they sprang to their feet and chanted, 'Allah is great, Mohamad is his Prophet,' and sat down again, like schoolchildren in front of their teacher. Mulla climbed into the pulpit and sat high up above everybody. He was our neighbour, the same man who frightened us. He began counting his long string of black beads and chanting out loud. I didn't know what he was talking about, and asked Farideh. She didn't know either. I put my head inside Shaba's chador and asked her what Mulla was saying.

'It sounds like gibberish. What is it?'

'He's reading Imam Hosein's funeral sermon.'

'But I don't understand it.'

'It's in Arabic.'

'Why not in Persian?'

'Be quiet. You mustn't speak here. I'll tell you later.'

Everybody shook their heads and looked miserable. I understood some of the things Mulla chanted. When he said something, the women began to cry out loud and beat their breasts under their chadors. Mulla cried out in Farsi, perhaps to make sure everyone understood:

'Brothers and Sisters, tonight is the night that Hosein, the dear son of our Prophet, the precious Imam, went to fight the Yazid, the enemy of Islam, in the hottest desert of Karbela, and was killed, together with his family and children.' In an even more miserable tone of voice he continued, 'Brothers, Sisters, cry on this night of mourning. Women, cry for Hosein. Ah, Hosein . . . I sacrifice myself to you, I immolate myself to you . . . Ai . . . Ai . . .' There were sounds of sobbing. Women began to cry out, wailing under their chadors and beating their breasts. The moaning sound grew louder and more overwhelming. Mulla continued to cry out, 'Women, cry for your Imam; men, beat your chests, our dear Imam is dead . . . cry louder, cry louder,' inciting the men and women to cry and sacrifice themselves for the death of Imam.

The women had pulled their black chadors over their faces and were completely hidden in darkness. I was puzzled. Was I supposed to cry? I couldn't. There was nothing sad in it except seeing the black-veiled women crying so loud and beating their breasts. They were so sad, I could cry for them, just like them. They looked like sacks of charcoal on a cart, which, when the driver pulled the cart, jostled to and fro. Farideh and I and Shahin imitated the women and pulled our chadors over our faces and tried to feel miserable and beat our breasts too.

Mulla declared that his sermon was finished and he was leaving. The women calmed down and sighed in relief. Tea was brought in and offered to Mulla first. He chose some cakes and sweets, and after him the men helped themselves to the cakes, dates and zolbia out of the big round china dish. We were still waiting to be served with tea. Only after the men had finished their tea and had eaten as many cakes and dates as they wanted, were the women served. A woman brought in the black tea first, then the cakes and the zolbia. But they were served in a box, not on nice china dishes. The women passed them round, but there wasn't enough cake so each woman broke a piece in two, to make it go further. The zolbia was passed round. This was my favourite sweet, but before it reached us it was finished and the empty box was simply handed back by each person. Most women didn't eat there but took the food home. What Shaba had taken she put in a clean white handkerchief and said, 'We'll take it home and eat it with the others.'

We left the rozeh and didn't wait for the sermons by other mullas because Shaba was afraid that my father's meeting might finish early, and he would be home before us. The alley was dark, and we found our way by the moonlight, me clutching Shaba's chador, and following her.

'I hope Father hasn't come yet.'

'No, I don't think so, his meetings are long nowadays.'

'Why doesn't he like Mulla and mosque and rozeh?'

'Well . . .' she sighed deeply. 'God knows, I wanted my children to worship God, to be good Muslims, but this happened to them in Russia. They are all godless.'

'But I like it, it's fun, I see my friends, we have nice cakes and sweets . . . Why did you cry like that, beating your chest?'

'It is the anniversary of our Imam Hosein's death. We must cry for him, he had such a hard and unhappy life.'

'I tried to cry like everyone else, but I couldn't.'

'Sometimes I can't cry either, but then I remember my children's death, my husband's funeral, and then I cry.'

'But that was a long time ago. Wasn't it?'

'Yes, it was. But still it makes me sad.'

'Do you like crying?'

'I don't know, but I feel much lighter after a good rozeh.'

'Most of what he said, it wasn't in Farsi.'

'No, he read Arabic; the Koran is in Arabic.'

'Do you know Arabic?'

'No, I don't read or write even in my language.'

'Well . . . So . . . how can you cry if you don't understand it?'

'I can guess, I have been listening to it for so many years now, I know it by heart. It is the same story repeated every year.'

'Why can't he say it in Farsi? I would understand it then.'

'The Koran is in Arabic, it is a sin to translate it. A good Muslim must learn it and practise it as it is. We must pray in Arabic too . . . Soon you must pray too. Homa, you should be a good Muslim woman, should go to the mosque, pray three times a day, and remember God all the time, not like your father and mother, godless people. Will you?'

'Yes, Shaba, I like the rozeh, I like my chador, I want to veil myself all over. I will be a good Muslim like you.'

She caressed my head tenderly. I loved her. She was so kind to me. I must learn Arabic, pray three times a day – once at dawn – fast for a month in Ramadan. I thought, how can I do all this? I'll surely be fast asleep at dawn. It's a difficult job to be a good Muslim. I liked the rozeh but I couldn't cry. I should cry, they would throw me out if I didn't. I suppose I could pretend, like tonight . . . but how could I force tears out of my eyes? Perhaps I could use my saliva to wet my eyes when nobody was looking. I repeated these thoughts many times in my head.

Nineteen

In summer my father would take the whole family out for a day's picnic to an orchard belonging to one of his friends. It was near Vanak, where my father's factory was. Vanak was a small village outside Tehran, in the north west. It was beautiful countryside and although we only went there once or twice a year, the pleasant memory stayed with us for a long time.

Everybody worked hard for the occasion. Shaba and Mother would prepare food for two days in advance. They would cook a large pot of rice, make vegetables, fried meat and cutlets, and pack fruit and a large watermelon. The journey was tiresome but interesting and we looked forward to it for days in advance. Each of us would carry something. Father usually carried some light blankets and rugs under one arm and a huge watermelon under the other. Shaba and Mother carried the well packed food bags, plates and saucers. I carried the tin kettle teapot, swinging it to and fro and enjoying the responsibility.

The year before we had got up at the crack of dawn and were soon out of the house. We walked to the railway square, Father in front, Mother behind with bags in both hands, holding her chador with her teeth, with us clutching on to her chador. Shaba was in between, sometimes in front, sometimes stopping and resting for a few minutes before catching up with us again. We got the bus in Railway Square and it carried us a long way to the north, towards Shimran.

Here it was hilly and the air was very cool. It seemed as if Tehran had two seasons, one for the rich northerners, the other for the poor southerners. The cool air refreshed us, and for a day we forgot the dirty, dusty heat of our streets. Shimran was beautiful, everything that a beautiful place should be. It had tall leafy trees on both sides of the streets, along wide narrow streams taking the clear blue water from the nearby Albors mountains to the streets, watering the lines of trees on the wide pavements. The houses were huge, beautifully made in white or pink marble. Each house had a huge garden with flowers climbing everywhere, on the building, over the walls, and red roses hanging down above the doors. Shimran was green, lush-green everywhere, even on the mountains where we could see trees growing. Some of the trees were so old and so tall that I had to bend my head right back to see their tops where they joined the clouds. People were clean, joyful, well dressed. Even the children had new clothes and shiny shoes on. Some were in a little park, playing on swings and see-saws. We must have looked a sorry sight in this gorgeous setting.

'Aah . . . so many lovely trees here, and such fresh air. I like this place, can we take a tree home and plant it in our street?' I asked Father.

'No, silly, we can't. It is beautiful, isn't it? It's because of the mountains.'

'Can we have a picnic here. It's a good place, isn't it? Where can we find nicer than here?'

'No, we can't.' He stopped and pointed to somewhere in the distance.

'You see that huge white marble castle in the distance? That is the Shah's Palace. We couldn't have a picnic anywhere around here.'

'Is all of this place the Shah's?'

'No, not his alone, he shares it with some other rich parasites, his family, the government ministers.'

'They have a lot of room to themselves.' I was amazed, as were Mother and Shaba, who were just gazing at the scenery. The white house, deep in trees, stood at the bottom of the mountain. Father's swearing interrupted our calm enjoyment. He soon ordered us to move on to get a bus which would take us to Vanak.

In Vanak we met Father's friend and he took us to his orchard. It was a massive space lined with mulberry trees, each heavy with ripe fruits. We made a home under the shadow of a few trees, put down our rugs, samovar and dinner. When everybody sat down to make tea and have a rest, Hamid and I ran off to play among the branches and bushes. Down the orchard we stopped speechless before an astonishing sight. I squeezed Hamid's hand, and said, 'Look, see, what are they doing there?'

'I don't know . . . they . . . are shaking the mulberries,' Hamid said. We stopped there and looked on. A few men and women, who looked like Shaba in their village costume of colourful long skirts and beautiful headscarves, were standing and each holding a corner of a huge white sheet under a large mulberry tree.

A man had climbed up a ladder, which was leaning against the trunk of the tree. He stood in a fork between several heavily laden branches and was busy shaking one. Showers of mulberries were pouring on to the white sheet. The sheet was as white as snow and the mulberries were white and ripe. They looked like white snow flakes falling in a snow landscape, heaping up a little snowy hill.

The man shook more branches, and the women who held the sheet moved around the tree until it was stripped of all its fruits. The man climbed down and everybody put the sheet down and began to box the fruit up for the market.

That day we ran around, with bare feet on the green earth, warm beneath our feet, and the blue sky above us. We ran through bushes and branches, ran after yellow and green grasshoppers and red and blue ladybirds, followed the ants' trail to their nest and looked for birds' eggs, chasing after birdsongs. There was no limit to our adventures, no barrier before us.

'Let's take these ladybirds and the grasshoppers home. I can put them in a jar . . . these little blue flowers too, pick lots of them!' Hamid said with excitement.

'I want to take these fruits, wild strawberries, mulberries . . . cut these bunches of flowers, big bunches of them, to put on the mantelpiece.' I was so greedy that I wanted to gather them all up and take them home. Hamid said that we couldn't, we had enough to carry already and Father wouldn't like it anyway.

Here there was no living room, no door, no knocker, no walls, and we had the vast open space and the fresh air and the green trees all to ourselves. The white mulberries, wild strawberries and other fruits we had never seen in our part of the town. I loved it. There were big green almonds cooled in fresh water and fresh walnuts in water, small yellow cherry-like fruit, black mulberries in their thick juice, and so many other things that I just ate and didn't bother to find out any names or how they grew and where. We picked them fresh from the trees and ate them, we searched for them on the ground, washed them in the spring and gobbled them up. In the heat of the summer day nothing was so pleasurable and satisfying or tasty as fresh cooled fruit. Mother said we would get diarrhoea, eating so much fresh fruit, because our stomachs weren't used to it. We didn't have room to take any advice in. We couldn't. The pleasure was beyond us, and we didn't limit ourselves on that limitless day. We were greedy, yes, but we were here this once only and we might not afford to come here again, so we went wild.

This was the one day's holiday that we had had the summer before.

This summer we sometimes spoke about the previous year's picnic in the mulberry orchard and hoped that we would be able to go there again. From the beginning of the long summer days we kept reminding our father. Shaba wasn't so keen because she considered it more as work for her, rather than enjoyment. But we pushed her and encouraged her to ask Father. He was very preoccupied each time she raised the issue: he said that he was very busy now, we should postpone it. We waited and he postponed it for too long, and one day he said he wasn't sure whether he could take us this summer at all. We couldn't insist any more, we felt very disappointed and sad.

Shaba's kind heart felt for us. So after some thought she said, 'Don't worry, that man is no use to anybody nowadays, he's got enough to think about. I will take you out. We will go for a day pilgrimage to the Shrine of the Shah-Abdol-Aziz [a holy place south of Tehran] . . . how about that?'

Mother heard it, sniffed and left the room in disgust. 'Seeing graves is now our summer holiday, what an entertainment, what a bloody waste of a life.'

Shaba didn't like what she said. She raised her voice, 'Well, if you don't like it don't come, stay here, stay at home. I'll take the children . . . She doesn't like anything I offer. She refuses even without thinking that it could be fun. Ah . . . such a woman, so high class . . . so fucking condescending.'

Mother was out in the yard. I went closer to Shaba. 'I'd like it, let's go to Shah-Aziz for a picnic. It's a different place, isn't it? What is it? and where is it?'

Shaba smiled. 'I must ask your father, he will also turn his nose up. I don't understand what the world has come to.'

How and when Shaba asked Father's permission and got some money out of him, I don't know. Perhaps it was one of the nights that I went to sleep early and didn't hear the argument.

When everything was ready and we were going, early on a Friday morning, Mother decided that she wanted to come too. It was better to be in Shah-Abdol-Aziz than to be at home doing the housework or being with Father, she concluded. Father hadn't been quarrelsome when we were packing the night before. It seemed that he was resigned to it, either because he couldn't influence Shaba or because she was a waste of his energy and he didn't want to bother at all.

Early on Friday morning, when the sun was pale and grey, we

woke up, bursting with excitement. We had a quick breakfast, although I didn't feel hungry at all. We set off. This early in the morning our alleys were very quiet and clean. We were the only people who were walking there – we could hear our own footsteps.

Railway Square was quiet too. Only some scattered street sellers were putting up their stalls and getting ready for a Friday market. We went to the other side of the square, opposite the bus stop for Shimran, and got a bus for Shar-Rey. Shaba said, 'Thank God we are early and we can have a seat.' That was really true: buses were always so packed, like sardine cans, that people quarrelled with each other over empty seats. We sat down and hugged our packed picnic. We were loaded down with rugs, a samovar, food, plates, and each of us was carrying two bundles, except Mother, who had Vida in one hand. I sat next to Mother and hugged my bundle. It was wonderful, I could look out of the window. The bus was jerking and coughing so much that Vida fell asleep fast. It was a long journey and the bus was slow, stopping at every bus stop.

At a huge crossroads we turned into a long wide highway. The sun was out now, pale and yellow, covering the pavements. This road was crowded with lorries and coaches. The roadside was green now, planted with aubergines and courgettes. There weren't any houses, except a small mudhouse here and there. I saw one by a large farm, and close to the house there was a pile of rubbish, tyres, tin cans and papers. Some dirty kids were playing outside the house. There were countless flies around, buzzing in the air, swarms of them sitting on the rubbish and covering the children's faces.

'Mother, are we leaving Tehran? It looks like the countryside here, deserted, like no-man's land.'

'Yes, it is a poor village; most of the people are agricultural workers. The worst slums of Tehran are around here, many children die of diseases every year.'

'It looks very dirty – the gutter's black and full of rubbish; all sorts of flies, everything is in ruins here, except those huge chimneys.'

'Yes, it is a tragedy. Shar-Rey is an ancient city, over three thousand years old, and it was a capital city six or seven hundred years ago. It was a prosperous place, a centre of art, science, literature. It had the largest manuscript library in the Persian Empire, and when the Muslim Empire defeated the Persians they burned something like fifty tons of books, manuscripts and its entire medical library. That's because they considered everything besides the Koran, and any other language besides Arabic, anti-God, therefore useless. The city was attacked and destroyed many times

123

by Arab conquerors, by Genghis Khan's army and the Tatars. It was razed to the ground. The destruction was so great that no other king bothered to reconstruct it. Now it has a shrine, and it is known for its cemetery. That is why it looks like a hole, the sewer of the north.' Mother was patiently telling me this. It was so unusual for her to talk so.

'Why did people burn the books and smash the buildings? It was nasty and cruel.'

'Yes, it was. The Arab army did it for Islam and God, the Monghol did it for money and treasures. Their soldiers, like any other soldiers, liked capturing lands, people, and their money . . . men are like that, everywhere . . . But listen, while Shar-Rey had a wise woman running it, the Monghol army didn't dare capture the city. They got it only after her death. Then they killed seventy thousand people, massacred them.'

'Why? . . . Were they afraid of her?'

'Yes and no . . . because she told them that she would defeat them, and they were afraid that if they were defeated by a woman's army, they couldn't bear the shame. So they attacked Rey only after her death.'

'Oh gosh . . . really? She must have been like your grandmother, strong and wise.'

'Mum, what are those long brick chimneys, far away?' I pointed them out to Mother.

'They belong to the cement factory.'

'But they are so tall, and there are so many of them.' Mother didn't answer me. She was looking into the distance, lost in deep thought. The chimneys were scattered around: from the top of each a cloud of black smoke came out, swirled around in the sky and lost itself in the blue clouds. Behind this distant smoke a round, golden minaret appeared. It grew taller and taller the closer the bus came to it. It was a magnificent sight, its yellow surface shining under the sun. Looking at it hurt one's eyes. There was a metal figure of a hand in the middle of the minaret, its five fingers opened to the sky. Another, smaller minaret soon appeared. We were there.

We got out of the bus, our bottoms hurting from sitting so long in one place. We had arrived at the crowded centre of Shar-Rey. We still had a long walk before we could get to the shrine. Shaba directed us, telling Mother to wear her chador properly and cover her face tighter. I tried to hide my face under my chador too, pleased to look like all the veiled women around us. It was difficult to walk fast, especially when we were carrying heavy packs. I was told off for walking so clumsily and slowly. It wasn't fair, I wasn't used to wearing a chador.

We followed each other and walked along the narrow pavement. There were amazing crowds. The streets and the pavements were covered with street sellers, each with their wares spread out on the ground. I could see the best kinds of cucumbers, slim and tiny, fresh, long aubergines, fat red radishes, small courgettes – all were sold on the pavement by the farmers themselves. The shops were loaded with huge trays of cakes, of apricots, raisins, pistachios, almonds, walnuts, hazelnuts and cooked salted chickpeas, all mixed up together – the most delicious traditional Persian confectionery. We saw them piled in big baskets in front of the shops. There were also large pots of fresh yoghurt, cheese and honeycombs. Shaba said that the food here was very, very good. It was all fresh from the farmers, all grown in good soil, no nasty chemical yoghurt or factory cheese.

'The bloody town farmers milking the cows with machines . . . what on earth is happening to the country?' she complained. When we passed some green vegetables that were kept in water, and fresh spring onions, Shaba said that we would buy some to take home. 'They really look fresh and appetising – not now, on the way back,' she said.

We passed a long, roofed corridor lined with kebab shops. Mother said, 'I wish we could eat kebab here for dinner. The kebabs here are famous for being the tastiest and the best in town.' I was walking, and looking around in a sort of daze, there was so much to see, so many different things, such a great variety of food. I nearly went cross-eyed with amazement.

We arrived at a wide wooden door rich with writings and carvings. It was wide open, and Shaba and Mother began kissing the carvings, so I followed them too, kissing the hard, rough wooden door. The yard was large, with a round hoze in the middle. Some men were sitting on the side washing their elbows and faces, and cleaning their noses very loudly. Now that both Shaba and Mother had covered their faces totally, I could hardly recognise who was who. I too pulled my chador over my face and hid myself under the veil. We walked up a few stairs, took off our shoes and gave them to the attendant on the corner. There was a huge, glittering hall before us, it's floor covered with soft Persian carpets on the ground, and tiny mirrors on the ceiling. While Shaba and Mother were kissing the walls and the doors I looked at the high ceiling in astonishment. It was such a beautiful work, it must have been hard to fit all those small mirrors on the circular, uneven surface of the ceiling. I saw the lights of thousands of mirrors broken and reflected in each other. They shone and glittered all around the hall. The doors were made either of carved wood or wrought iron. The mosaics inside the room, of Islamic design and colours, were fantastic too. Everything there was magnificent, eye-dazzling, artistic. But Mother and Shaba weren't looking. They had covered themselves completely in black. It seemed this art was oppressive to them.

Crowds of men and women were holding on to the metal bars of the shrine and kissing them, and walking around it in a circle. There was a huge chandelier with many golden lights and bulbs, hanging in the middle of the ceiling. The room itself was small, square, and very crowded. The shrine was a large platform, square and high above the ground, with heavy metal bars all round it. Some women were sitting in the room reading the Koran. Shaba held my hand tight and said, 'Kiss this holy shrine, kiss it.' She lifted me up for a second and I saw through the metal bars, beyond the glass cover, piles of money, coins and notes. Tons of it had been poured in on the top of the holy man's tomb. It looked like a big open-top treasure chest. I stared at the money and forgot to kiss the shrine. Shaba squeezed me again: 'Kiss the holy shrine, my little girl.'

Breathing a deep troubled sigh, Shaba and Mother went round the square tomb two or three times, kissing the metal bars again and again and mumbling some holy ayeh repeatedly, 'Oh, dear Imam, I immolate myself for you, please forgive us, forgive our great sins, help us. You are generous . . . you are magnanimous and forgiving . . . Ah, dear Imam, I immolate myself for you.' Both Mother and Shaba were repeating these words with pain and continually asking forgiveness.

We left the main shrine chamber and passed through some other rooms, which were decorated with elegant and magnificent carpets. Walking on them was a pleasure, they were so soft and warm to our bare feet. We walked through a room full of mullas standing around with books and waiting for customers. A group of men beyond them were praying in loud voices to God and his Imams. In a women's prayer room many women in black veils were sitting praying. They all had their faces covered too. They were reading some ayeh to themselves in very low voices, which sounded like flies buzzing around. The room was dim and dull, with black cloths covering the walls, and there were no windows to let the light in, only a pale

126

flicker from the ceiling. As we passed them they looked like squatting bats, content that they could still see, but waiting. We passed down some corridors, with mirrored ceilings, through carved wooden doors. A group of mullas were standing in a passage with the Koran in their hands, inviting people to have the Koran or a rozeh read to them for a fee. I saw a fat mulla who was counting a thick wad of money notes. He had his back to us, but when he saw that we had seen him, he quickly put his money away and said to Shaba, 'I can read you a rozeh, the rozeh of the poor oppressed life of Imam Reza and his sister Masomeh, their terrible life in exile – it's cheap.' Shaba thanked him, but she said that we didn't have enough money for the fee. She would have liked one if we could have afforded it. In another corner two women were bargaining with two other mullas over the high cost of a rozeh.

We crossed a small green courtyard, and went to a burial room of the Ghajar kings. This room was very large and square with a high ceiling, and many windows around the walls which opened on the yard. There were tombs of many kings here, with their wives' and children's graves scattered around, raised up above ground-level. Mother directed us here and showed us the Ghajar kings' graves, but Shaba wasn't interested. Most of the tombs were raised on a dais, with a marble stone over them and photographs of men in fantastic clothes with big long moustaches propped up beside them. There were no photographs of women. There were many chandeliers hanging from the ceiling, and golden candles sticking out of the walls. Each grave had a long board covered in writing above it on the wall. Mother was reading some of these while I looked at a white marble statue of a king above his grave. Mother came over to me to explain who he was. She said that he had been killed by a revolutionary during a pilgrimage. He was an extravagant, old-fashioned tyrant. When he came on a pilgrimage here, only women were allowed in. He also had numerous wives and was infamous for marrying very young girls. The assassin was dressed as a woman and hid his gun under his chador. He approached the king to give him a letter, and as he took it, he pulled the gun from under his chador and shot him. This was the beginning of the constitutional revolution of Iran. And here I was, standing by his marble statue: it was so well made, it looked just like a man lying down.

'This statue took a long time and the work of many sculptors to carve. The making of the body and its curves . . . it is said that it was so difficult a piece to fashion that one sculptor killed himself because it kept breaking.'

'Really?' I couldn't believe it.

Shaba was impatient and came over to us. 'Have you finished blathering on about these kings? I'm thirsty and I want some tea.'

'All right,' Mother said. 'Let's go and find somewhere quiet to sit in the yard.'

Shaba told me that when they were alive these kings lived in comfort and luxury, that they never went hungry. 'Even now that they're dead they're still lying in the lap of luxury! The bastards!' she complained, 'I'm not even sure I can afford to die . . .'

'Oh, Shaba, don't talk about dying, you must live until you're a hundred and twenty,' I told her to cheer her up.

'No, I'll be useless then, a crone, an old woman.'

'You'll never be useless, Shaba, you'll still be doing the cooking, the nice chips you make.'

Everybody laughed; I didn't know whether it was at what I had said, or at Shaba's chips.

In the large courtyard, at the end opposite the graves we had seen, there was a space where families were having picnics. We found a clear spot and spread out our rugs, the food, and the samovar. Here it was cool and shady, but over the unprotected graves the sun shone hot and bright. Shaba lit the samovar to make tea: put the charcoal in it, lit it, and puffed and puffed till it began to glow red. I took the pot to get water from the tap on the hoze. After I had fetched the water, Mother sat me down and put Vida on my lap. I had to look after her while they made the tea.

Vida was crawling about on all fours and trying to get away. I bit into my peach, indignant at having to look after her while Hamid could just go off and play and climb trees. Vida was quiet, but never still; each time I sat her up and gave her her rattle she would play with it for a minute, then throw it away and start crawling. I was tired of watching her, I wanted to pinch her, but couldn't. I didn't know what to occupy her with all the time. It was boring and I wished Mother would finish soon and come to my rescue. I watched children playing nearby with a ball. Shaba was having her tea now, she couldn't wait till after dinner. I tried to pass Vida on to her lap, but she said she was too tired after carrying all the tea things, and she wanted to rest and have her tea. And what about me then?

Soon dinner was ready and I was free to leave Vida. I called Hamid and he came with his dirty hands and sat down at the sofreh. Many of the families around us were much larger, had more children and had their fathers with them. They sat on long colourful sofrehs eating huge meals. We were small and didn't have much variety of food on our sofreh but we did have a small watermelon after dinner, red with black seeds; juicy and cool, satisfying our deep thirst. After dinner, Shaba took the plates to wash by a gutter on the other side of the courtyard. Mother was preparing Vida's food. I was about to sneak away when she called me to take the nappies and help her wash them. It was bad enough not being able to play, but worse to help wash Vida's nappy and smell it. This was what I hated most. We went to the women's toilet which had a single tap for washing. There was a queue of many women and children and babies waiting for the toilet, and to wash under the single tap. There was no sink, only a tiny drain, so that all the toilet floor and even outside was wet with dirty water. There were only two toilets and no rubbish bin. The place was dirty and there was refuse everywhere, in a heap in every corner. The toilets were dirty too. Children had shat on the corners and there was hardly any space to put one's feet down among all the lumps of shit there. Mother refused to go in at first, but soon we had no choice but to use it.

'It's so dirty here, all that money donated to this place. Why don't they use some of it towards the maintenance of the women's toilet?' Mother protested, but the other women were silent or just said, 'Pough . . . terrible . . . what a horrible smell,' and went away.

After Vida was washed, had fed and sucked Mother's breast, she calmly slept in her arms. Shaba was drinking tea and resting, and Mother put Vida down to sleep on the rug. An old man was smoking water pipes near us. Some women were chatting further away. I wanted to go around and see things. Mother wanted me to have an afternoon nap. I didn't. I managed to go and join Hamid.

There were fresh flowers on some of the graves, and some had trees planted next to them. Some of them had photographs, mostly showing very young people. A few had marble stones on them, others had only a clay surface. There were writings on them I couldn't read, so I just looked at them and touched the stone. The afternoon sun was at its hottest, pouring down over the ground. Even under the trees' shade the heat was unbearable. The sun was moving on to our rug and we had to move to a more shady patch.

It was time for afternoon prayers and our afternoon nap. Shaba went to one of the dark rooms by the shrine to pray. She said it would be doubly good before the eyes of God to do so in this holy place. Everybody around us was either resting or had gone to join in the prayers. By the round hoze, men were doing their ritual washing before beginning their prayers, washing their hands, elbows, faces, and cleaning their noses. Mother didn't pray, she didn't even pretend to. Perhaps she was tired and couldn't be bothered . . . I went to ask her to come and read me some of the grave inscriptions. She was reluctant, but I begged her and pulled her hand, and she came. 'Now, where shall I start? This woman is Fatima Saiedi, fifty-three years old. This man is Karim Robabi, sixty-four, this a young man Hamid Habibi, twenty-five years old, who died in Shahrivar in 1948, this man also in Shahrivar in 1948, and this other young man . . . they were all killed in the street-uprising . . .'

'What does street-uprising mean?' I asked Mother.

'Well, it means . . . people . . . workers want more money, better working conditions.'

'Why? . . . and they die for it?'

'No . . . only when the government refuses . . . or the factory owner calls the police, then there is a fight and some people die.' I thought the police only looked after the traffic, people crossing over the road.

'Mum, come here please, there's a big one here with a beautiful tombstone . . . Who is this man? His tomb is very big. He must have been a very big man.'

'Yes . . . this man is Satar Khan, one of the leaders of the constitutional revolution of 1906–1911.' The tomb was marble, shiny black, flecked with spots of grey. The writing was engraved in big letters, deeply etched in the marble, but there was no picture or statue of him. It was raised above ground-level with two layers of steps on each side. It looked a plain, but large and interesting grave.

'My grandfather fought with them, my grandmother talked about the street-fighting.'

'Does he also have such a big marble grave?'

'No, he doesn't, not all of the men were rewarded so well, only a few.'

We rested on the rug for a while, Mother sitting and brooding. It seemed she was drowned in a sea of thought. Sometimes, when everybody was asleep, Mother would stay awake like this, thinking. Shaba was asleep. She was so still she looked like a lump of untidy blankets. Soon I was feeling sleepy too.

The shrine was quiet. The afternoon in that big, beautiful pilgrimage cemetery was still and stagnant. The hubbub and the crowd of the morning was stifled now. Everything was strangely silent, a kind of awesome silence, as if the power of the dead had taken over the living – who, in identifying with the dead man in the shrine, had laid themselves at rest, sacrificed, beneath his feet.

When the afternoon sun was getting paler and paler, we began to pack. Everything was neatly parcelled into eight bundles. Hamid carried the teapot in one hand and Vida's tiny pillow in the other. I carried two bundles, one in each hand. After a while I began complaining that I couldn't walk properly because of the chador. Mother said I should wait a bit: after we had left the premises of the holy shrine and were into Rey Square, I could take off my chador and put it in one of the bundles. This made walking and carrying much easier. Shaba and Mother stopped before the street market salesmen and bought some fresh radishes, long black aubergines and a pot of farm yoghurt before we climbed up into the bus.

In the bus only Shaba could sit down. She held Vida and some of the luggage, the rest we held, standing in the back of the bus all crumpled and squeezed up with other men and women throughout the two-hour journey. The passengers were packed so tight next to each other that everyone pushed someone else with each jolt of the old coach. It was airless and cramped and men were crushing women. We were very tired and got more tired by standing up all the time and being pushed around.

It was sunset – red and blue, cool and fresh, an early hour of the evening – when we climbed down off the bus with relief and began the last part of the journey: the walk home. Mother turned to Shaba to complain about the bus journey:

'That crowd in the bus was killing me, you know.'

'Thank God because I am an old woman, a man always offers his seat to me.'

'What a cheek they have: one bloody big one behind me, he looked like a wrestler or something, was pushing me all the time.'

'They're like that, especially on such a long journey: they won't miss a chance to rub themselves on us.'

'He was pushing his bloody thing in my back, all the way.' Mother straightened her chador and showed Shaba part of the material, saying, 'Look, it's wet, bloody wet, he emptied his filth on me.' Shaba had a look but she was not surprised.

She said angrily 'My God, filthy, they're filthy men . . . Ah men . . . men . . .' She stressed the 'm' as hard as if she meant murder, or as if she wanted to spit and slap them on the face. 'Keep quiet about it, wash it tomorrow. Go to the public bath and have a ritual wash, get yourself cleaned up.'

'Those filthy men, they only come to the Shah-Abdol-Aziz for that, they'll do anything for that, anything at all.' Mother spat on the ground.

'Shush . . . be quiet and don't mention it to Eby, he would get mad. You know how highly he thinks of his honour . . . Just forget it.'

Mother gripped her chador in her hand. She walked home, head down, angry, muttering insults, grumbling bitterly.

But I had had a nice day. Not nicer than last year's in Vanak, but better than being stuck in our alley. I had seen lots of new things and new places, and Mother had talked to me. I didn't like the women in the shrine – they looked sad, sulky and dull. The cemetery was very sad too, all those dead men and their happy pictures. Tomorrow, I would tell Sara about what I had seen today and ask her why the man in the bus squeezed himself and made Mother's chador wet.

Twenty

       I was standing in the shade of the wall watching the children playing in the middle of the wide lane. Sara had a small kite in her hand and was running down the lane flying it. She turned back at the bottom and came up again to her friends. She flew the kite down the lane and up, again and again. I was watching her, it was exciting. Shahin was there too, and she tried it, taking the same route as Sara: she also went down and came up the lane a few times. The kite was a triangle of yellow paper and was very shaky in the air. It flew very low and was wobbling and turning around. It would be good if it could fly high, really high. I imagined it flying high, straight and right above us in the sky. They didn't know how to make it fly high.

Hamid and some other small boys were running after a cat, feeding it, teasing it, catching it by the tail and holding it upside-down. I didn't like that. I didn't like the games the little boys played. They were very naughty, always a nuisance to the animals. If it wasn't the goldfish, it was the alley cat or the pigeons. Sara was still running up and down. Her feet were coming out of her plastic

132

sandals and slowing her down. They were very busy playing and were far away from me. I was watching them. I wanted to try the kite too. It was dancing in the air, shining under the sun, yellow shade on yellow, so beautiful. If I could fly it, I would make it go high, very high, as high as the pigeons. Sometimes I dreamed that I was flying in the sky, going wherever I wanted to, like a bird, and stopping where I liked. It was a pity that I couldn't fly when I was awake, going through the clouds like the birds and landing on top of the trees. When I had told my dreams to Shaba she had said that I should stop looking at the sky – my head was too wrapped up in the clouds, but Mother had said that perhaps I liked travelling and I would be travelling a lot when I had grown up. This could be the interpretation of my dreams. Shaba had said that, if so, it meant that I would have to find a rich husband who had enough money to take me around the world. Perhaps I should become the wife of the British Ambassador. Everybody had laughed at her saying that. I still wanted to fly like a bird more than anything else, and wanted to fly the kite high. I was still watching them and dreaming when Sara noticed me and flew the kite up to where I was standing.

'That's a nice kite.'

'Yes, my brother made it.'

'It doesn't go very high, the string isnt long enough.'

'If you want it to go high you must run fast too – running fast would make it go higher.'

'My sandals aren't good for running, my feet slip out all the time.'

'Can I try it?' I asked quietly.

'Yes, have a go . . . but where is your chador? Don't you wear it any more?'

'No, I can't play with it on. I don't wear it now. I don't like it any more.' I took the string into my hand, and fumbled with it. 'It isn't very long.' I wanted to run fast, very fast, and make it go high, the highest. Sara stood in my place. I held my feet tight in my cotton sandals and began to run as fast as I could. I turned back once quickly for a second to check how high it was – not very high but much better. I went up and down twice. Sara took it from me and she flew it again. 'Let's try to make it go high! We can,' I told Sara before she ran off. 'It's good now, high, much better, Sara.' We each took a turn flying the kite, and each time we ran faster and it was more exciting. Sara had had her second go and it was my turn. I went to her to take the kite, but she was going to run again. I caught her arm and tried to take the string from her. She wouldn't give it to me.

'It's my go.'

'No, I haven't finished yet.'

'You had two goes, it's my turn.' She was pushing me away and I got angry and told her, 'It's not fair.' She hit me and said, 'It's my kite anyway.' I pulled her hair and pushed her off me. 'It doesn't matter, you had your turn.' She pulled my hair and hit me again. We had a bad fight: she was stronger than me, grabbed me hard and pulled my plaited hair. I screamed with pain. It hurt me badly. I was very upset,crying with pain, but I couldn't hurt her. I screamed, and cried, and threw her bloody kite, which was now in my hand, on the ground and trampled on it and ran towards our home. The roots of my hair were aching and my knees were bruised. I got into our yard crying noiselessly while tears ran down my face. I crept to the living room, avoiding everybody, and hid myself behind the bundle of mattresses. I cried quietly and swore at Sara and vowed that I would never speak to her again.

I wanted to go to my mother and complain about Sara; ask her to take my side and beat her up, but I couldn't. I knew she would thrash me, but if the same thing had happened to Sara, her mother would have defended her to the last. She always came out into the middle of the lane and created a fuss if one of her children was beaten up by someone. It wasn't fair on me. Sara was a bully. A hard, selfish bully, just because she was bigger than me and she could thrash me. I hate her guts, I thought, I won't speak to her till she begs me to. Sara you're a bully, you're a donkey, I'll ride on you. I will write this on her wall and their door three times tomorrow. I will take my own revenge.

Mother had been grumbling for a few days that she needed money to buy herself underwear and a dress and a decent new black chador. She wanted to go and visit her aunt in the coming Eeid (feast day). She couldn't visit them in her usual rags. She was nagging to Shaba that she hadn't bought herself a new dress for a year now, her underwear was in tatters, her knicker elastic so loose that her knickers were constantly falling down and she had to hold them up with one hand when she went shopping, in case they dropped in the middle of the road. Her stocking holes were beyond repair. If Eby insisted that she had to cover her legs, wear stockings, then he should buy them, shouldn't he? She was ashamed to pay a visit to her relations in such a shabby outfit. What would they say? 'Look how Eby keeps his wife.' At first Shaba ignored her complaints but when Mother went on talking about it to her, she argued that new clothes were not so necessary in life. She should be patient, it was a hard time, the men didn't get enough wages and they had problems in the factory. Why did she want to be pretty and dolled up, and whom did she want to impress? Their daily argument over the issue dragged on, Mother insisting that her needs were important too. Why did he spend his wages outside the house on himself, his friends, why couldn't she have her essentials? If she had worked as a maid, she would be clothed at least, she wouldn't have to argue that she needed a pair of knickers. Shaba gradually came around and agreed with her, after a lot of persuasion. She agreed that Mother in ragged clothes would be bad for Eby's reputation and honour. She should have some decent clothes, to look respectable in when going out. Shaba said to her that she would take her side and stick up for her in front of Eby, but she should wait till pay day and then ask Eby the night before his wages were due. She also advised her to be patient, persuasive and calm.

'Don't aggravate him. If he refuses to pay for it, I will ask for you.'

Mother had asked him civilly the night before pay day. He hadn't argued, didn't refuse, just postponed the issue till he got his wages on Thursday, and said it would depend on how much he got paid anyway. Mother said she wasn't sure if he even listened to what she had told him.

Today was the promised day. Mother was already talking about how to ask for it. She was repeating it while pacing up and down the room doing the housework. 'He must be going out drinking again . . . he must have his hot water and soap pretty fast . . . he must give me some money tonight.' Mother was speaking to herself. Shaba was pottering about, doing the tidying up, and listening to her. She insisted that Mother shouldn't be so persistent, so demanding.

'You will get it, don't worry, if not tonight, perhaps next week.'

But Mother was impatient, and she was preparing his washing facilities with a kind of nervousness about her. I was sitting in my corner and playing with my cat's cradle, tangling the string between my fingers and untangling it, listening to what was being talked about around me.

Father came in nervous, his long bony fingers gripping the crumpled newspaper. I timidly said 'salam', and watched his movements. He looked gloomy. Shaba asked him if he was all right and had had a good working day. He mumbled that there were

135

demonstrations everywhere and the workers might go on strike. He asked for his hot water and soap. Mother lifted it from the cooker and brought it in.

'Homa, get my towel,' he said. Shaba was already looking for it.

'You sit down, I will give it to him.'

I was standing and wanted to get it and give it to him to please him. I was disappointed. I looked around for something else to do for my father, stood there and waited for a while, but there was no need for me as Mother and Shaba were around him and seeing to his needs. He must be going out again.

'Are you going out tonight?' Shaba opened up the conversation.

'Yes.'

'So you don't want to eat? Give us some money before you go out then, tomorrow's housekeeping money, because if you go out tonight you'll pour it all away down your throat and come home dead drunk.'

'All right.'

'I want some money too. You said that you would give me it today . . .'

'What for?'

'To buy myself some clothes. I told you last night.'

'But not this week.'

'I can't wait any longer. Eeid is near. I want to go and see my aunt.'

'What is all the rush for? Wait a bit longer. Everything is so difficult now. It's a revolutionary period. Money doesn't come easily.'

'I've no decent clothes to put on. You've got your wages, give me some money tonight.'

'Silence . . . You don't understand . . . you don't earn the money, you're talking off the top of your head.'

'You're going to spend it on your friends, in a cafe tonight, drinking, spending a week's wages in one night. When it comes to paying for the housekeeping or towards my expenses, you get stomach pains.'

'I am not going to a cafe, I am off to an important meeting, and talking about your clothing needs is making me late.'

'What's the difference! It ends up in drinking, clubs, women . . .'

'But why on earth do you want to dress up to see those Muslim cranks anyway?'

'Don't insult my family, they're a thousand times better than yours.'

His face grew hard and the lines on it got deeper with anger.

'Stupid slut, don't talk rubbish . . . They're soft in the head, still living in their dream land by the Prophet's side in the Arabian desert. Your aunt half lives in heaven already. I bet now she is siding with Mulla Kashani and the clergy against Mosadegh.'

Shaba interfered on Mother's side, 'She only wants some money to buy herself some clothes, so what's wrong with that? Leave Mosadegh out of it. You're going to spend this money tonight on aragh, well . . . it's not nice for you if she goes to see her relations in rags, is it?'

He had finished washing, a pile of his dirty overalls, dirty sweaty socks, T-shirt and pants piled in the corner of the room by the washing bowl. He moved to put on his clean shirt and tie, which were lined up tidily within his reach.

'She had better stay at home, better stay away from those middle-class parasites.'

Mother hated her family being insulted like that.

'Don't insult my family. They're respectable middle class people. You . . . you've got no family . . . except peasants!'

He pulled up his trousers, zipped them up. 'Shut up! How dare you? Bitch!'

'I won't, why should I?' Mother murmured.

'Where's my bloody shirt . . . my tie?' he yelled.

Shaba, bending, moving around in despair and disgust with the turn of the conversation, held up the clean shirt and said, 'Here, put it on and get out before you create any more trouble . . .'

'My tie as well,' he yelled. Mother stood up looking for the tie. 'Has it been washed and ironed?' he demanded.

Mother was grumbling, 'Every Thursday night you wash, dress up and get all powdered up to go out and enjoy yourself. I have to stay in here, all the time in this hole.' The black robe covered her body, but the moaning anger was clearly heard through her teeth. 'It is under your nose.' She held the tie up: 'This bloody tie I wash, iron, and have ready for you – why?'

'Give it to me,' he cried out.

'Why? I won't. Get it yourself.' She moved away from him.

'I'll beat the hell out of you.'

'This bloody tie, a worker . . . peasant . . . you don't need to wear a tie.' She was near the door. 'Take it!'

She was mad with anger, as if blind and totally indifferent to the consequences of her action. She threw the tie across the yard and looked as it landed in the narrow gutter and got wet. Father

watched it, shocked for a second. Then he rushed to her, screaming
'You bitch, slut, prostitute, just because you want new clothes to go
on whoring yourself . . . you . . .'

With the landing of the first slap on Mother's face, fear took over
my body. I closed my eyes, shivering as if it was cold and I was in
the middle of a freezing winter. When I opened my eyes again
Mother was under his feet being trampled, kicked from left to right.
Heavy blows from his big hard feet were landing on her body, like
the butcher mincing the meat in a grinder with all his might. She was
there on the floor, bent and squashed, wrapped in her black chador,
crying, moaning and swearing. He was mad with fury, power, like a
big wild boar.

Shaba's attempt at interference was pushed away. He threw her
into the other corner and when she came back, hurt but intending to
push him away from Mother, he hit her again.

'Get your fucking hands off her, leave her alone. Get out, out of
the house.' She was pushed away again by Father. 'Hit me, you
bastard, showing your manhood . . .' Shaba was an old woman with
a deep voice and bitter anger and a sarcastic tongue. 'What a strong
man you are . . . hitting a woman. Stop it, you fucking big prick, get
out.' But it didn't stop, he got more mad and went on beating
Mother with hands and feet in every direction, again and again,
bruising her all over. 'Get out! Get out! Stop it, you big prick, you
madman, you love beating a woman, your prick loves it . . . animal
. . .' She moved towards him and pushed him away with a sudden
thrust, putting herself between him and Mother, making a shield to
protect her. 'Get out, get out of this house and don't ever come
back, you bastard.'

I was in my dark corner, sweating, holding on to my knees and
leaning against the wall. I wanted to disappear, not to see, not to
hear. I was so afraid, so terrified that my teeth were chattering.

The wall behind me was hard, I was pushing against it, wanting to
hide, to disappear beyond it. My body was shaking and fear was
growing like a ghost inside me. I hated it. I hated these continuous
bitter fights. I hated this house, this family life. I hated everything
about it. There was no fun, only misery and pain in our family. I
wanted to run away.

Mother's bitter crying came from beneath her black veil. Sobbing
between clenched teeth, calm but shaking like a bird that had been
shot. Her long deep groans were bitter, she was hurt badly, and
bleeding inside. 'I am wasting my life here, my family, my future, I
have been wasting myself here for years. What on earth for? What

on earth do I live here for? My youth, my energy, my body, I am wasting them all in this house, with this ignorant, barefoot worker, this stupid man, this animal.'

Shaba, who was also hurt, lay crumpled in a corner, holding her knees and swearing at him. I was relieved that he had gone out, that the fight was over for now. Mother, still wrapped in her black veil, was crying; she looked so low, so down.

I looked at her and saw her in many shapes, many different figures: her body had many different and versatile shapes. Sitting breast-feeding Vida, holding her in one hand and stroking her with the other, she looked like a goat being milked, upright. Stretching her arms and legs while ironing she looked like an octopus in a hot sea. Sitting over the washing bowl she resembled a dough which is constantly being kneaded. Bending to clean the rice, she looked like a tortoise that has a long, slow, troubled passage to plough. Stretching her body to rest, with her legs extended, relaxed, I remembered her when she was told, 'Open your legs, open your legs, it won't go in.' She was the door which was rammed through and broken into: invaded. Standing veiled in her black chador, walking out to go shopping, she resembled a tall chimney which is burned, blackened to the core but still functioning; she still had to remain firm till the old house was pulled down. She was solid and stable yet changing; remained motionless and yet moved on, all the time becoming something else, somebody else. My mother was a combination of so many things all at once, so many people all in one; so many events all in the space of a day. I wondered what she was and why – why she was so manipulated, and so violated.

Twenty-one

The next morning when I woke up the room looked empty, so bare, dull and bleak. Sadly but quietly I got up and saw that Mother wasn't there. Mother had left us. She had taken Vida with her too. She had left me behind.

139

The house was very quiet in Mother's absence. Shaba went on doing all the housework. Hamid was in the yard, sitting on the edge of the hoze with his stick, pushing it into the water, chasing the goldfish. I was wandering around Shaba, questioning her about Mother, trying to help her. She said she didn't need any help and I should go and play outside. But I didn't want to go and play outside, I wasn't in the mood for playing.

I went inside the room to look through my notebook and do some writing exercises. I started to write, 'Mother brings in the water.' I couldn't hold the pencil straight in my fingers. I did only a few clumsy lines. I got annoyed with it: it was too boring. I put it away and started to play with my five stones, throwing them up and down, up and down. But soon I got bored with them too. I felt very slow, didn't want to do anything. I wanted just to stay there, in my little corner, in the gap between the heap of mattresses and the wall. I sat and did nothing, leaned my hands on my crossed legs and thought about what had happened the night before. Fear came over me, as if it were happening all over again. The arguments, the shouting, the insults, the tie landing in the gutter. Father battering Mother, on and on. Her crying, her insults, and where is she now? When did she go? Perhaps she left us when we were asleep. When? Many things happen when we are asleep. Adults get up to some odd tricks. Where is she? Is she coming back? When? I was very gloomy.

Shaba came into the room, called me and said that Shahin wanted me to go out and play with her. I went out, and found her with Farideh: they had drawn a big hopscotch and wanted me to play with them. I agreed. The squares were drawn with white chalk on the black asphalt. Shahin started, throwing her stone across to square one and jumping, hopping in the single squares and landing in the doubles till the last one, and then coming back. After Shahin, it was Farideh's turn, after her, mine. We hopped on and on. I was slow and missed a lot. They had longer turns than me and so won most of the squares and put their names on them. As I didn't have any squares of my own, and they didn't let me in their houses, I couldn't go on playing. I had failed. I got unhappy, left them, and went home.

Farideh came to see me later and console me; it didn't matter that I hadn't won the hopscotch game. She asked me where my mother was. I said I didn't know. She went on questioning me. She was nice to me, put her hand on my shoulder and touched my hair. She asked me to go to her house and play in their empty room. I remembered the nice time we had had there together. I liked her, but I wasn't in a mood for any game. So she came to our sitting room and went on questioning me.

'Where is she?'

'I don't know.'

'What happened?'

'Father and Mother had a fight. Father beat her up, she left home.'

'Has she taken your little sister with her?'

'Yes, she has. I miss them very much.' Tears were gathering in my eyes. She went on touching my hair and holding my shoulder. I liked her company, her touches. It was warming me.

'Don't worry,' she said. 'She will be back soon. Thank God, I don't have a Father, my aunty and my mother fight too, but they don't hit each other.'

'Yes . . . she only wanted some money to buy herself a new dress and a chador to go and see her aunt for Eeid.'

'Perhaps she has gone to their house then.'

'I don't know, in her old clothes . . . She wouldn't. She wanted to go there in her new clothes. That's why she was beaten . . .'

'Has she got somewhere to stay? She can't sleep in the street.'

'I don't know, perhaps somewhere else . . . but where? I can ask Shaba.'

Shahin asked me, 'Would she know?'

'Perhaps.'

'Was your mother angry with her too?'

'I don't know. Shaba took her side and she was beaten too.'

'Your father beat his mother too? . . . Oh, that's bad.'

I told Shahin that I wanted to go and ask Shaba where Mother had gone. She wanted me to go and play with her, but I wouldn't. Shaba was by the kitchen cupboard, bending with half of her body inside the recess, cooking. She told me that I should wait for a few minutes – when she made some tea for herself, I could have a cup of tea and she would talk to me.

Shaba made the samovar ready and put the tea glasses by her and sat down for a few minutes' rest. Hamid was sitting next to her. He seemed upset as well but he didn't talk much, didn't ask questions either, he just went on pestering the goldfish. Shaba poured us tea; I didn't usually drink tea, I didn't like it much, like Mother. She didn't drink tea much either, but she sat down with Shaba at tea time. Shaba had mixed the old tea that she always kept in a bottle with the hot water from the samovar, rather than making fresh tea.

So the weak yellow tea in front of me didn't look very welcoming. Shaba looked as if she were sitting up and smoking the water pipe, but she wasn't. She just held the tea like a pipe in her hand, and seemed to inhale it down her throat.

'Have some bread.'

'No. Where is my mother? where has she gone?'

'She hasn't gone far, she'll be back soon.'

'Where is she sleeping? Is she sleeping in the street like those beggarwomen in the railway, who hid their faces and their babies under their chador?'

Shaba put her half-sipped tea down and came to me, put her arms around me, gave me a big hug. Her hands were large and rough, old but strong hands with lots of deep lines in them.

'No, she won't sleep in the street. She is not a beggar, she has very rich relations. She is very comfortable there and she'll be back soon.' Shaba was very kind to me, spoke very gently with warmth and love and gave me lots of kisses on my cheeks and my face. She also kissed Hamid in case he felt jealous. Why couldn't everybody be kind and sweet to everybody else at all times? I asked myself. Shaba gave me a sweet from her small but much treasured knapsack. I chewed the comforting, delicious morsel. It was nice and shut me up. I didn't question her any more.

After dinner Hamid went out to play. Mother wasn't there to stop him. I stayed in the room, Shaba insisting that I should go to bed and have a long afternoon sleep. 'Sleep is good for you; forget your problems,' she told me. She always wanted me to have long afternoon and evening sleeps when something was wrong in our house.

But I couldn't now: I was sad for Mother. Shaba busied herself washing the dishes, and I asked if I could help her. As usual she refused, saying I wouldn't know how to do it properly, I would break them, or I shouldn't bother anyway as she always had to do them. But when I insisted, she wanted to please me, so she let me do the rinsing of the dishes in the hoze. I rinsed each plate thoroughly in the greenish water and saw the goldfish coming up many times. They were alive and still sailing on. But I wasn't in the mood to splash water on them or chase them with my fingers. I remembered the night when Father had had a fight with Mother over her bad cooking and thrown the copper tray with everything in it in the hoze. I had thought they were dead then, but the poor goldfish had survived even the hard blow of the copper tray.

142

Days passed by. The house remained quiet and sad, everybody looking thoughtful except for Afagh who was angry and showed her anger to us. She told us if we hadn't excited Mother she would be a happy woman. I didn't like her, she was never kind to us and now that we were sad, she blamed us and hurt us by saying that she was happy that Mother had left us. The only good thing about her was that because she was on her own, and her son only came home on Thursday nights to stay until Friday afternoon, she went out a lot and stayed with relations or travelled to her home town. So we didn't see her much. Thank God, if she had been around every day, she would have told us off all the time.

Nowadays, when father came home Shaba served him when he washed, cooked his dinner, and washed and ironed his clothes. She toiled hard, doing all my mother's share of the work as well as her own. Father had everything done for him, so he didn't miss Mother. Shaba grumbled to him, criticised him, blamed him, but he didn't really listen to what she said, just told her to stop talking.

'Women talk so much, God,' he would cry out.

We were very quiet, didn't say much, but he played with Hamid, putting him on his lap and joking about his willy.

'So she has gone, left you alone to your willy. This willy is big, that is important. Don't worry, my son, you will be a big man soon,' he would go on.

I wanted to say something, to talk to him too, but I couldn't find the right words. I didn't know what to say or how to say it. I only took his orders, gave him water, his socks, his ashtray, whatever he asked me for. He didn't talk to me about anything else.

Shaba started a low-voiced conversation with him to soften him, and advised him to go and bring Mother back.

'I can't do all the housework, it's too much, it's breaking my back. You should go and bring her back.' Father was reading the paper and was lost behind it. 'Leave that bloody paper. Listen to me for a second. The house needs a woman. I can't be your wife, and look after your kids, I've done enough of that.'

'What the hell are you talking about? Let her stay in her stupid relations' house: I don't give a damn.'

'No, you wouldn't, you just want your suppers ready. Stop reading that rubbish – it's all lies, it's irrelevant and deceives you! Put your house in order, man!'

He put down the paper in anger and shouted, 'What do you want me to do?'

Shaba lowered her voice again. 'Go and bring her back home.

This house can't manage without her. She only asked for some money. After all, it is your fault.'

'No, I will not, let her rot in there, she's a bitch, my children don't need her. They'll grow up fine, fuck her.'

'I told you, but you were young and hot-headed and didn't listen. I said you were a peasant boy, a worker, marry somebody from our class, our own village, a peasant woman who won't have a long tongue, and such middle-class ideas. A woman who'll do as you want her to.'

'That's rubbish, she wanted me, she was in love with me. Have you forgotten how she was crying in their orchard when her father refused to consent to our marriage?'

'These youthful romances end up here, in big stupid fights over clothes! You knew she wasn't used to rags, old clothes, the veil, housework, that she had a private maid. Why did you give her all those promises of rose gardens?'

Silence . . . Shaba continued when Father didn't attempt to answer her. 'She has always had the best, not like me: I put up with my old clothes, I like them, they are part of me and my past, I share some good memories with them, but she is young and wants nice things. Why shouldn't she?'

'She knew I was a worker and couldn't afford to provide her with those luxuries, she can't wait . . . there are so many problems in the country now, there's a shortage of food. I have so much to do in the factory, so much is on my mind, the country is on the verge of a revolution, we must work hard to make it happen – I can't bother about a woman's flimsy wish. Let her get lost.'

'That's not right, she has needs too, you know.'

He unfolded the newspaper and started reading it. Shaba went on to do the housework and didn't say anything else, only mumbled under her breath.

It seemed he read the newspaper from cover to cover. There were lots of pictures, and many photographs of people among them. I peeped at them. Most showed people carrying banners and flags, their mouths wide open and their fists waving in the air. It looked as if they were very angry and threatening something. Sometimes Father read out a piece of news in a voice loud with excitement or called Shaba to listen to it: 'Look: look at this picture, everybody is demonstrating against the Shah, in every city, even in our home town.'

Shaba just shook her head. 'Yes, I know. I saw a bunch of heated men shouting and walking down the road this morning when I went shopping.'

'It's great.' Father was very happy.

'It seems men have nothing else to do. It's about two years now that they've been crowding the roads and screaming their heads off. The shopping takes twice as long these days: you've got to wait till the road is cleared.'

There was a knock on the front door. Father went to open it and we heard his loud laughter and greetings. He and Amo Salim came in, arms round each other's shoulders. They were smiling and chatting happily. Shaba greeted them and they sat down to talk. She started the samovar, as usual, making tea for the guest.

'Have you eaten? . . . or just come from work?' Father asked Amo.

'Come from work, but I had something on the way.'

'Eat with us then, dinner is nearly ready.'

'Yes, that's right, stay for dinner. But we need fresh bread, Eby. Go and buy some bread,' Shaba told Father. Bread-buying was Mother's job, but now she wasn't there to do it.

Amo looked around and noticed somebody missing. 'Where is our bride?' he asked. Shaba lifted her head up and made a face to show that something was wrong. Amo stopped speaking.

Father changed his indoor pyjamas, put on his outdoor trousers and quickly went out, saying, 'Well, I'll be back soon.' He was annoyed that he had to go out to buy the bread.

As soon as he had left the room Shaba sat down close to her elder son to give him the latest news. After a quick exchange about Salim's wife and kids, she told him about the incident. 'Oh, it was terrible, your brother is empty-headed, a real bully. All that politics he talks about hasn't improved his thinking or his life but has made him more stupid, more useless when it comes to problems at home. She only asked for some money to buy herself clothes. He beat her to a pulp, every domestic argument ends in a fight and then he beats her. What can we do? She's been away with her relations for a week now.'

'If she is wise she won't be back,' Amo said. 'But then, when she left for a year many years ago she came back – that was her fatal mistake.' Amo was upset now.

'Don't say that, what can she do in her aunt's house? She needs her husband and her kids.'

'Eby is irresponsible, showing off his muscles like a young bully-boy. You don't beat women, God has beaten *them* by creating them women.'

'Of course, Salim, she does have fancy ideas, she isn't totally blameless, she wants new clothes, wants to visit her relations, and then she shouldn't insist when he refuses. But she does. She is stubborn too . . . you know.'

'Well, she's from a good family, she has never been hungry, has never been cold or in rags. Eby knew all this when he was courting her: when he decided to elope with her. He must have forgotten his promises. No, it is no use,' Amo continued, 'Eby is careless towards his family.'

'I always said that we are poor, we mustn't mix with a class above us. Look at the mess he has made. He doesn't even pay the rent regularly. He says, "I don't have it, rooms are for living in, not for making profit from . . ." If you don't have money and it's a hard time why do you go drinking every week? I don't know, Salim . . . he's very wrong, I don't know what to do.'

'Well, he doesn't take care of his wages, he wastes them, this hard-earned money. He doesn't take care of his wife either. All he does now is the Party work, and goes out with his mates . . . He is too irresponsible. He doesn't deserve that woman.'

'I'm getting old now. I'm not well . . . I cannot run this family, look after these kids, my eyes are weakening day by day. He must go to bring her back. Please, Salim, ask him to do so. He will listen to you, please.'

'But he must change himself! What is the good of her coming back? It will happen again. Why doesn't he give her the housekeeping money? She can save bits from it for her clothes.'

'Well . . . I get the housekeeping money – she is too young and can't be trusted with the housekeeping money yet. Anyway, he pays us a meagre amount and he thinks if she gets it and does the shopping she'll steal some of it for herself. When I'm not here, and she does the shopping, she has to write down what she has bought and show him the goods and give him back the pennies left over. She even has to write down the children's lollies. Thank God he doesn't ask for the lolly sticks to be kept as proof.'

'Damn it . . . damn his attitude!'

The door clicked. Shaba elbowed him, 'Ssh . . . don't forget to ask him,' and they stopped the conversation. Shaba busied herself with the preparation of the dinner.

Father walked in with two large, hot, brown sangak in his hands. He was cursing, 'Bloody long queue, all women, they push you and get served first. Stupid baker didn't serve me first.' Shaba answered him back quickly:

'You never buy the bread, he doesn't know you, perhaps he thought you were a newcomer to this area. When I buy the bread they always serve the men first. They are taller and not hidden under the chador. They come late and are served first . . . some poor children stay there a long time and have to shout to be served. They get the worst deal. I usually push them to go first if I'm not in a hurry.'

'Get the plates, Homa,' Father said. I moved fast and went to help Shaba spread the sofreh and put the plates on it. Shaba brought in the dinner of red beans. We ate it slowly and politely. It was tasty and warm and we enjoyed it.

After dinner Shaba started the samovar for tea. She put mine and Hamid's bedding down and told us to go to sleep. Hamid was already falling asleep, but I wasn't sleepy and sat playing on the bed.

'The tea is ready, Salim, come and have some.' Shaba offered it to him.

'Fresh tea, Shaba?' Father asked sarcastically.

'Yes, the tea is fresh, stop complaining.' The tea was served in small shining glasses to the men. Then Shaba poured some of the cold tea from her old bottle and mixed it with hot water for herself.

'Shaba, drink some fresh tea with us,' Salim protested.

'I like my tea: fresh or old, it is still tea. You have the fresh tea, you are men working hard outside home.'

'She'll never change, she likes the old piss water,' Father said angrily.

'There is incredible news in the paper. Have you been following it?'

'Oh yes. Who doesn't? I've got to buy the paper at seven o'clock because it runs out ten minutes later.'

'Yes, good . . . it is the revolution, people are rising up, it's great. Anti-imperialist demonstrations everywhere, getting bigger and bigger and bigger . . .'

'Mosadegh's position is still not very stable,' Amo said. Father took out a small bottle of aragh and as soon as Shaba left the room to wash the tea cups, they sat down to drink it.

'The good news is that the Shah is leaving the country, going on holiday. If he goes he's had it.'

'Yes, there are many good things happening,' Amo shook his head. 'But the country also faces incredibly complicated problems as a result of the American and European economic boycott – and there is the possibility of foreign intervention.'

147

'But the people's consciousness is growing fast. The most important thing is to get rid of American and British interference in our internal affairs – then we can manage our own business.'

'I'm not so sure . . . Mulla Kashani's religious lot is more dangerous than American imperialism. And the Americans and British have compromised on sharing the oil between them and are now united against Mosadegh. Mulla Kashani and Zahedi from the army are also uniting against him. He, like you, underestimates the internal reactionary forces.'

'I have never said that I wasn't anxious . . . I get frightened too. Many, many a time. But I don't want my fears to undermine our struggles.'

'It's just that you are so damn sure you have the answer.'

'It may be so . . . but I never said it would be easy getting there.'

'But . . . it looks to me imperialism is not what *you* are talking about, not just rate of profit! It's . . . it's . . . this Britain, the country of the gentlemen of the world, with Europe's oldest monarchy . . . that Her Majesty's Government actually pays groups of roughs, semi-criminals, to go around beating up Mosadegh's supporters! That is what makes me sick, really sick . . . that is imperialism, real imperialism.

'And they did worse than that in Ireland,' Amo finished quietly.

They drank more aragh and talked more politics. They agreed and disagreed until the conversation turned to personal lives and family matters.

'What's happened to Mina? Where is she?'

'Well . . .' Father lowered his voice. It seemed he didn't like the question. 'She's with her relations.'

'Man . . . aren't you ashamed of yourself, beating her up? She's a jewel. You don't deserve her. It's a pity she is wasting her life in your house.'

'She asked for money and didn't wait. She has very expensive tastes and no patience, and a very, very quick tongue. She answers me back and insults me.'

'Why don't you take care of your wages, why don't you give her money for her clothes? Where should she get that money from? Hey? You are the husband, aren't you?'

'But at this time? It's a bad time, the country is in turmoil, I am busy with so many other issues . . . She nags me all the time.'

'But man, you took all her money, remember, when you were unemployed. You put all her jewellery in a scarf to pawn it. You couldn't fit it all in one. What did you do with all that wealth? Spent

148

it. It's not fair . . . now you beat her up every time she needs money. Oh, you are thankless. God doesn't like it.'

Father drank his glass fast and looked very serious and gloomy. He didn't like his brother's censure. 'I don't think it's right to let the woman take over. You let your wife make most of the decisions in the family, have the housekeeping money and go out freely. This makes women loose. You're soft.'

'Nonsense! I can't do the shopping and take the decisions about the children. I'm not there . . . But Mina, she was an independent woman, earning a wage. You told her, don't go to work, stay at home and look after the home and the children. But man . . . it's wrong what you have done to Mina. You've got to change yourself, repent, go and bring her back.'

'It's the usual thing whenever we have arguments or fights: everybody takes her side, because she has come from a middle-class family, always led a privileged life; she has money and influential relations now, she still has everybody's support and sympathy. Nobody is interested in knowing what happens to me at work; how I earn the wages that I earn. My problems are considered mine, and if I can't sort them out, if I am without a job or my wages are low, then I'm not man enough. Afagh and Shaba say that and despise me because I'm a worker.'

Before Father went to bed, he turned to Shaba and said, 'Go and bring Mina back tomorrow. I will give you some money, the travel cost, in the morning.' Shaba nodded with a smile on her face.

Twenty-two

Shaba was sitting on the floor cross-legged, with her much treasured knapsack spread open in front of her. She took out her only best blouse, waistcoat and scarf, and told me, 'Go and have a wash and get dressed. We're going to bring your mother home.' She was taking me with her. I was pleased, I didn't want to stay behind like my brother, who was going to stay in Sara's house.

I went to the courtyard to wash my hands and face in the hoze.

The sun was coming up, and daylight was gradually spreading over the roofs and the yard. The cool breeze of the early morning touched my face. It was a fresh morning. I splashed the water on my face. It was cool too.

I was waking up. The goldfish came to the top, bouncing under the bright sunlight, swallowing streams of water, racing each other. I didn't try to catch them, I wanted to rush to bring my mother back. I put on my best, my only, decent clothes and went to Shaba. She looked pretty and colourful in her long pleated skirt. Her waistcoat had beautiful hand embroidery around the edges. She never wore anything else but her village costume, it was her pride: 'You look nice. Aren't you hot in that long heavy skirt?' I asked her.

'Your mother's family are respectable, I have to look well.'

'But aren't you hot? Isn't it difficult to move around in the street?'

'No, I feel at home in these, I'm used to them. I don't think I could wear what the city women wear: just a dress showing their knees and legs. Aren't they always cold? I would feel cold and bare if I wore a dress showing my legs.'

I didn't understand what she meant, but I knew that no woman dressed like my grandmother in our area. I liked it, but when we went out together I was embarrassed and hid behind her chador, because people called her a Turkish peasant woman.

We walked to the bus stop. Shaba held her grey cotton chador tight around her face, only one eye could be seen. I hung onto her chador and followed her. Her skirt was too long to be covered by the chador, so when she walked her long pleated red and white skirt moved gently. The streets were wide and large, with many cars and many people walking in every direction. What a crowd! Shaba said it was market day. We passed the fruit stalls, with their heaps of yellow melons and green watermelons. The vegetable stalls were full of aubergines, courgettes, bright green parsley and fresh spinach, and the iced-water and sherbet stalls looked most appetising. I immediately felt thirsty. The fruit and vegetable stalls by the market looked colourful and luscious. Women were passing by and doing their shopping. In their full-length black chadors, they looked like walking chimneys, inside out, heavily blackened.

The streets are a different world altogether. Unlike houses, they are on the move, colourful, changing slow and fast, spacious with a sky above and the horizon beyond. It is so different from the atmosphere of the house where I stay all the time. Our house, our alleys are small, limited, walled and private. Inside the house it is dim, stifling, monotonous. I can't do much there, just mess around, look at the goldfish in the pond and try to catch them. I can't be active, it's too small. I have played hide and seek with a friend there, but there aren't many unknown corners where I can hide. We know all the corners in our rooms, they aren't large enough to hide in and everybody knows them anyway. There's nothing new about it, and there's no space for creativity or invention. It's fun to be out, so much to see, so much to look at, so much to notice.

I was still in a hazy state of rapture at this living, exciting world when we got to the bus. I was so fascinated, looking, watching, gazing, that I didn't even notice when we got there. It seemed such a short walk.

Shaba bought a ticket and we boarded the bus. It was half empty and we found a seat by the window where I sat on Shaba's lap. The driver was sitting on his seat and waiting for the bus to load up. More and more people came in until all the seats were taken, and even more stood in the back and in the passageway. The bus set off only when it was completely full. It started with a big noise. I could see a young man and a woman sitting behind us, she holding a small baby in her arm under her chador. He had his legs wide open and was smoking a cigarette. Every now and then he turned to her and checked they were all right. They never spoke to each other.

Many men were standing in the back, with one hand flung out holding the bar and a cigarette in the other. The women were mostly seated, and the men always offering their seat to women who had babies in their arms or shopping in their hands. Still, there were some women standing up, struggling to grasp the leather strap handhold with one hand and their black veil with the other. Two women standing in the passage had difficulty in holding their babies and their chadors and the leather strap all at once. Each time the bus braked they lost their balance and were jolted to and fro by the crowd. The air inside the bus was becoming smoky, hot and sultry. The baby behind me began to cry, the mother quickly pushed her head under the chador and soon she was quiet. Each time the bus stopped and some got off, more came in. It was crowded and cramped and there was no room even to drop a pin. In the end the door couldn't be shut and people hung out through it. There were some eleven- and twelve-year-old boys amongst them, who had their dinner packs in their hands and were on their way to work. It was so crowded that I could see nothing but outstretched hands and black heads, like aubergines in the market.

I was looking out of the window. This was the best part of the journey, sitting by the window and watching the shops and the pavements go past. There wasn't enough time to see and notice everything, except when the bus stopped at a bus stop or at a traffic light. Sometimes the bus jerked constantly, in great hiccups which made the shops and the buildings and the cakes in the sweet shops go bumpy and fuzzy. I was fascinated by the pavement scenery and my eyes were gobbling up all that I could see. Shaba was reciting pieces of the Koran, moving her lips. It seemed that she was nervous of the ride, the crowd and the men. She was calling God to help her to get through this journey without any terrible accidents or disasters.

The bus was jolting on and on with its heavy load. The heat was humid and the smoke unbearable. A woman shouted, 'Stop, I'm unwell, bus-sick,' but before anything happened she suddenly puked up. Heavy, sick yellow liquid poured out over the bus.

'Stop, get some water,' somebody else shouted.

The driver stopped, looked back: 'A woman is sick! it is nothing new, they're sick all the time . . . just clean it, I'm behind schedule, I can't stop.'

'They aren't used to the bus ride. They shouldn't leave their homes in the first place,' another man commented.

The woman hid herself under her chador, bent down as if she wanted to crawl under the seat and hide there. The bus set off. A few women offered hankies and cleaned up the yellow vomit. Everybody was gazing at her and the women. Some were shaking their heads, some showing their disgust with disapproving noises. A woman who was sitting next to her touched her shoulder and rubbed her back slowly, murmuring, 'Don't worry, it happens to everybody, don't take any notice of them.' The bus shook itself and went on, the sour smell of the vomit added to it. It looked like a cattle cart riding to its destination.

We got off the bus in a very crowded square, where many other buses had stopped too. Shaba grabbed my hand and held it tight. 'One gets lost easily here,' she told me. This was Shush Square, and here we took a bus to go to Rey Town, where there is a holy shrine. Shaba and I crossed the packed roads, street stalls, the crowded shops and market place, and walked down an alley on the way to my mother's family house. Shaba said that it was near here, and that they had chosen it to be near the holy shrine. By the side of the pavement there was a large space full of big stones. I saw some men hacking away at large marble tablets, writing names and dates on them. Shaba said that they were carving our gravestones.

We passed some smaller alleys lined with clay houses, and children playing in the street and the gutter, till we came to a better quarter which had nicer, brick-made houses, cleaner roads and healthier-looking children. Shaba told me that my mother's family lived on this side of the town. They were religious but not poor, middle-class people, who were educated and had never been hungry, never needed to wander around from city to city in search of work. Although Shaba liked their religious fervour, she resented their cosy lives.

Shaba stood at their door nervously, looking tired, hot, and sweaty. She straightened herself, tied up her scarf and chador. 'They have a nice house, God be with us,' she said, mumbling bits of the Koran in Arabic before she grasped the large door knob and knocked it shakily. A little girl from the neighbouring house opened the door, said a quick salam, dashed down to call my mother's aunt and disappeared. Shaba was warmly welcomed by the aunt and they exchanged long greetings while we were led in. Auntie directing us, we passed through the yard to the corridor where the rooms were situated.

'We are all in the basement now because it's cooler. Let's go downstairs,' Aunt said. I looked in all the rooms: they had large beautiful carpets, huge pine wardrobes and tall gracious mirrors. They looked meticulously clean. Auntie stopped at the top of the stairs and let Shaba, who was walking very slowly and timidly, go first. Then she turned to me, smiled, and helped me down, as the stairs were high and tall and my short little legs had difficulty in reaching the next step.

I saw my mother sitting in a corner, covered in a chador. I felt nervous and shy but when she smiled at me I dashed to her and dived into her bosom. I stayed hidden under her cotton chador for a while, not saying anything or doing anything. She touched my hair and gently kissed my face.

'How are you, my big girl? How have you been keeping?' Tears glistened in her eyes. She reached for a corner of her chador in case she needed to use it as a hanky. I murmured 'Fine', squeezing myself further into her lap like a baby animal in search of warmth and security.

Shaba said salam to Auntie more than once and excused herself a few times for her intrusive visit, a sign of her continuing nervousness. She was offered a seat at the top of the room as a token of the reverence due an older woman, also a gesture towards a guest. Besides Mother's aunt Hajieh, her older aunt Sharieh was in the room too. Hajieh was Mother's nearest relation, her mother's sister, a substitute for the mother that she didn't have. Sharieh was the older woman. She was Hajieh's aunt, but we all called her Auntie too. To make the differentiation we called her 'Small Auntie' because she was very small and very skinny. It seemed she had shrunk over the years. Mother said that she especially had had a tough life. When her husband was ill and paralysed, she had looked after him for years. Their elder daughter was epileptic too. After his death, she had had to devote her life to her daughter, therefore she couldn't marry; or perhaps no man would marry her, with a sick daughter. As she didn't have a home of her own, she rented a room on the top floor here and had been living with Auntie for a long time, paying rent to Hajieh's husband. She was a seamstress and earned her living working all day sewing relatives' and neighbours' clothes. Because she had to pay for her daughter's medicine she had to sew long hours into the night. Shaba said the poor woman looked like a sewing machine herself, crumpled and bent. We also had our clothes sewn by her. My mother liked the little patterns she sewed on them. She always wore beautifully made clothes herself. We told her that and she was proud of it.

Hajieh was different. She was younger, stronger, a wife and a mother who lived a relatively comfortable life. She was nice-looking, plumpish with a white skin. We called her 'White Auntie' sometimes. Shaba said she had never worked outside, had never sweated beneath the sun. She and her husband Haji (who like our Haji had visited Mecca) were very religious.

He had a shop in a bazaar and owned his own house. She could read the Koran and interpret it; she often read religious books on Mohamad and his family and advocated Islamic government vigorously. She had two sons. The eldest was about twenty-two, married, with a young baby girl. I didn't know whether the men were in or not, as they usually stayed away from the women's quarters. Perhaps they were in one of those nicely furnished rooms.

Shaba was sitting at the top of the room still looking uncomfortable, all the more so because she was different from them, as a village woman who didn't speak Farsi. Sharieh insisted that she should take off her chador and wear a 'home-chador', as they had many to offer the guests. She passed it to them unwillingly and waited for one to be brought to her, hugging her knees as if she were cold and bare, exposed to the whole world. As soon as she put on the new chador she looked more secure and confident.

'I'll make some sherbet for you,' Hajieh said.

'Oh, please don't trouble yourselves. I have come to ask Mina to come home. We would like to go home soon.' She was all apologies. I had to translate as they didn't speak Turkish. But still Hajieh insisted that because it was hot and we had come a long way, we needed something cool to drink. She went out to make it. Shaba and Sharieh spoke to each other about their health, and getting old which had no remedy.

Then Shaba turned to my mother and asked her how she had been keeping and why she hadn't come back home. Mother answered Shaba quietly at first, then she raised her voice: 'Why should I come back to be battered and insulted? . . . "Home!" What kind of a home is it?' She emphasised the 'h' sarcastically.

Hajieh came back with a tray of sherbet in her hand. Silence followed while the bright red drink was handed round to everybody. Drinking the sherbet quietly, Shaba continued with her plea. 'It's your home whatever happens, men are wild, we must be patient.' There followed a moment of polite silence; and beneath it a heavy atmosphere. I was too excited to drink.

I couldn't take my eyes off the tall tumbler and the pieces of ice dancing in the sour cherry sherbet. It was so cool and good. The silver tray sat there empty in the middle of the room. Hajieh asked, 'Is Hamid at home? Who is he staying with?' I had already told Mum about that.

'He is staying with one of the neighbours . . . I know that Eby has a foul temper, but you are a mother. What have the children done to be left uncared for?' Shaba was shifting around beneath her chador. She looked very nervous, unsure and uncomfortable.

'But he is a husband too, a man earning a wage. Why is he so constantly penniless? And he beats her. Why can't he mind his work properly and bring home his wages? We haven't given him a wife to batter and starve.'

'It is not manly to hit a woman. One expects more from Eby. Why don't you advise him?' Sharieh asked Shaba.

'What can I do? He hits me too when he is enraged. We mustn't aggravate him. We must have more tolerance, we have no choice. I have nowhere else to go. I am stuck there too.'

'It's disgusting. He beats me up. He insults me and my family. He doesn't clothe me. He doesn't even feed me. I can take care of myself. They are his children too. Why doesn't he look after them? Why should I care? Why should I waste my life?'

'Men are all alike – that foul temper, that horrible, dirty

language, that violence. We must understand them, they have a hard time in the factory. He gets up at five o'clock in the morning to go to work and doesn't come home till nightfall. It's a hard life.' Shaba said this while looking at Hajieh.

'But all we hear is that he is always on strike. That's not hard work.'

Sharieh echoed Hajieh and said, 'It is Mina's choice to go back. This is her house, she can stay here as long as she wants. But if she returns we want a guarantee that she will not be beaten again. He must behave himself and look after her and the children. It is not decent, God doesn't like such actions, it is disrespectful to him.'

Mother did not answer. It seemed that that was the outcome of the meeting. A long silence fell again. Mother looked older, her face grown lined and wrinkled with sadness. Hajieh invited us to stay for lunch and the afternoon nap, as it was nearly afternoon anyway and too hot to make the trip back home. They insisted we should eat with them. Shaba agreed and we stayed.

Women bustled about preparing the food. I unfroze myself from my mother's limbs, feeling more relaxed – the tension in my body was easing up. I relaxed my hands and feet, leaned against the wall, and sat there cross-legged looking around. My mother had got up to set the sofreh.

The basement was cool and dark, the only daylight coming through the tall stairway which led down to the room. If we had shut the door it would have been completely dark. The walls were low and painted white. A tall person had to bend. But it was all right for women, as they always bent when walking because of the chador.

Shaba was leaning on a large cushion, of which there were many around the room. There were also mattresses folded up on top of each other. Shaba looked on nervously while the food was being prepared. Chadors were shuffling about in circles, bending and unbending around the sofreh. Soon the sofreh was loaded with ghormeh sabsi stew, rich with beans, meat and lemon juice, white rice, tadic, yoghurt and cucumber, and a jug of iced water. One woman put something down, another added something else to it.

Suddenly we heard the sound of a man crossing the yard making noises, hem . . . hem . . . to let the women know that he was approaching. Soon he was coming down the stairs. The women quickly straightened themselves, tightening their chadors around their bodies so that only six pairs of eyes were moving around the room. He walked in greeting everybody; it was Banisadre, Haji's elder son. All the women were now standing up in his honour. He greeted Shaba warmly and asked her to be seated. She sat down, bending shyly.

He was a tall, gallant and powerful man. He was very well dressed with a tie on, the opposite of his father who wore simple clothes. He had a little beard, the sign of the supporters of Islam. He had been well educated in a religious school, spoke clearly and emphasised his words. He looked a tower of dignity, reverently holding a book in his hand as if it were bringing God's message. Shaba was so intimidated by the sight of this grave man that she could only mumble her words.

'How is Eby?' he asked her, looking at her directly.

'He is fine. He has sent me to come and take Mina home.'

'Has he promised to behave himself, or is he still up to his old tricks, distributing communist papers and agitating in the factory?' This was supposed to be humorous. They all smiled. He held out the book in his hand to Hajieh: 'A new book on Ali and his family; it's got some good bits on Mohamad.'

Hajieh looked at the book and touched it.

'Oh good, tell me what it says after you've read it.'

He soon excused himself and went upstairs. His meal would be served to him alone.

Lunch was delicious, and I ate a good deal of meat. My mother must have eaten well these few days over here. Light blankets and pillows were brought in after lunch. We all lay down, one woman next to another, close for the afternoon snooze. I saw Shaba was uneasy: she tossed and turned as if on a bed of thorns. But it was a soft and cosy bed, and I liked it. Obviously it was a heavy day for Shaba and she couldn't get to sleep easily.

Afternoon tea was not as luxurious, but simple and welcoming. Shaba, with her love of drinking tea, enjoyed afternoon tea most. Mother got up and put her things together, packing in the sombre mood of the traveller who is always on the move, uprooted constantly.

We left their house late in the afternoon when the sun was going down and the air was cooler. Walking to the bus stop, I held my mother's hand tight. Shaba said it was nice to go back to one's own home, and turning to my mother said, 'I feel uncomfortable in other people,s homes. Nowhere is like our own home.'

Mother bitterly said, 'Yes, but whose home and which house?' emphasising the 'h' contemptuously, a faint smile dying on her face. Perhaps she would be glad later on. Shaba said that she would be happy when she saw her son Hamid.

We saw the sign of the bus stop. Many women and children enveloped in black chadors were waiting there in a queue. We moved forward and placed ourselves amid the black-robed crowd waiting under the bus shelter. I remembered how Shaba had once said that women are like black coal: they are only used for burning, they are black and sooty. I huddled in the crowd, holding Mother's hand and feeling safe. There was no bus in sight but waiting there with her was comforting.

Twenty-three

Mother was back. Hamid was very happy and jumped around her all the time, I was happy too. I didn't want to go out to play. When any of my friends came to call me I said, 'No, I'm not playing.' I stayed with my mother inside the house. She was happy too. She played with Vida for a long time whilst washing and feeding her. Shaba was very nice to her, giving her tea and telling her not to bother about the housework. But Mother couldn't just sit down and do nothing. She wasn't used to it, but also, after so many days away, she had come back to a load of dirty clothes, sheets, undusted rooms, and a basketful of darning to do. She started quickly, going straight out to the yard. I stayed indoors to look after Vida and play with her.

The yard was boiling, the mid-summer heat was scorching. Out of doors it was so hot that Shaba brought in the cooker and started cooking indoors. Mother had difficulty in finding a shady corner to do the washing, and part of her body was always in the sun. She had loads of dirty washing in front of her. Her chador was making her sweat more.

Mother's washing took a long time. I got tired of staying in the room. Vida was tired and sleepy, so Shaba put her to bed. When I was free of her, I went to the yard and asked Mother if I could help her. She gave me a little corner of her washing bowl to myself with some socks, and I watched her hands to see how she washed, and tried to do the same as her. She handed me a little soap, but she was washing the dirty clothes with the bottom of a stocking, rubbing and pushing it hard against the dirty collars and cuffs.

158

'What's that inside the stocking?' I asked her.

'It's the small bits and pieces of soap which I collect and put in a stocking with a knot on the top, so I can use it like a bar of soap. But it's harder of course.'

'Why do you do that?'

'To save soap. It's too expensive to buy a whole new bar for each washing.'

'Were you richer in your father's house?'

'Hmm,' she smiled. 'Well, it was different.'

'How? What did you do when you were my age?'

'I didn't do much. I had a nanny.' She smiled again.

'Really? A nanny? What is a nanny?'

'Oh, a middle-aged woman who looked after me.' After a long pause, she said: 'I didn't have a mother, she died when I was two. So she was like my mother.'

'I'm glad I have a real mother. Were you sad?'

'I don't remember it. My grandmother was responsible for my upbringing. She liked me very much.'

'Did your father beat your mother too?'

'No, he didn't. She had him under her thumb.'

'Did he beat you?'

'No, he didn't, not all men beat women.'

'Do you like my father?'

'I don't know . . . it's difficult . . . you ask too many questions. Go out and play with your friends, go on, you don't need to wash. I'll be finished soon.'

Mother didn't like some questions and didn't want to answer others. She didn't talk much about herself anyway; so I left her alone.

I looked for my playmates in our lane. I hadn't played outside for a long time, and I hadn't seen my friends for a few days either. I walked down the lane and heard noises, shouting, getting louder.

'What's happening?' I asked a woman neighbour who was coming back with an armful of shopping.

'The streets are blocked. Men are demonstrating, they're shouting, "The Shah has run away abroad!", "Victory is here!". Everybody is happy,' she smiled, 'but don't you go there alone. The streets aren't safe for little girls. You know they might steal you. Go home, go and help your mother.'

I turned back towards home, but as soon as she went inside her house I turned back down Javady Alley towards the main road. The narrow pavements were packed with black-robed women and

159

children, and the street was full of men walking and shouting. I couldn't see them very well. I didn't understand most of what they were shouting about. The pavement was narrow and there was a wall of women's bodies lining it. I pushed some of them aside and squeezed myself forward with great difficulty, getting through the few tight rows to that edging the gutter. Now I could see them: there were many, many young men, some old ones, and some children there too. They were all waving their fists and sweat was rolling off their faces down their open-necked shirts. Some had banners, some placards with rough writing on them. They shouted, 'Let the Shah run away abroad', 'We want our oil', 'Mosadegh is our leader', 'Victory is ours', 'Down with British policies'. They were also carrying a picture of an old man. They were walking past me, so tall I couldn't see their faces properly. I had to look upwards, to bend my neck as far back as it would go, then I could see some of their faces, but not if they were also looking up, or looking to the side. I could see their trousers and their feet best. I had to stand on my toes and push hard to become a bit taller. The men looked hot, wet, angry, and very excited; they were shouting the same slogans over and over again. Most of their shirts were undone at the top, their bare chests showing; they had hairy chests. Some had tight trousers, their willies were bulging. A few men touched theirs.

I wanted to know more, so I turned to ask a woman, but she was too absorbed watching them. Most of the women were standing on the pavement and didn't join the demonstration; they didn't say much, just stood there watching the men go by. When they passed our road and disappeared, the women left the pavement and walked home. I went home too. Mother had just finished the washing and was hanging it out on the line.

Father was again engrossed in his paper, lost behind the large, brown sheets covered in huge headlines and photographs. I wanted to ask him about the pictures in the paper: they looked as if they had been taken in our street when the men were passing by. I waited until he had read his paper, finished it and folded it, and started to smoke a cigarette with his tea. He looked happy, but deep in thought, and I wasn't sure he would want to answer me, but I plucked up some courage and came out with it.

'Father, what does the paper say? . . . those pictures . . . what are they?'

'Well now, why do you want to know? Go to bed, you're too young.'

'Everybody is talking about it. Who is the Shah? What is the oil story?'

'Yes, it all started with the oil story . . .'

'Please tell me, Papa . . .'

'Now . . . how can I put it simply? How will you understand it and remember it . . . the oil story?' He lit himself another cigarette, and searched for words.

'Now, the political situation in our country is very serious and bad because the British Navy is in the Persian Gulf . . .'

'What's wrong with the British Navy being in the Persian Gulf?' Shaba butted in. 'They like cruising around in everyone's water. They come from generations of fishermen. Didn't they say in the Soviet Union that they even went cruising there after the revolution?' she persisted.

'The British Navy doesn't just cruise around, you stupid woman, it's a sign of war, invasion.'

'What war? What invasion? Why should the English invade a poor country like Iran? Perhaps it would be better for us then, after all. They have a queen. She would run the country better than the Shah.'

'Don't talk nonsense,' Father told her. I was getting annoyed with Shaba. She had to put her nose into everything, and anyway, she didn't know anything about politics.

'It's because of the nationalisation of the oil industry. We want our oil for ourselves, and they want compensation.'

'Why can't we share it with them, if they need oil? We've got loads, haven't we?'

'Yes, but it's not like that, it's not so simple.'

'So it can be simple. Pay them what they want and stop the war. Why doesn't Mosadegh pay them?'

'Tchh . . . hell . . . You know how much they want? Practically all the money in the country. We don't have it. If he has to pay, we'll be paying back the British for the next two hundred years. Just to compensate for our own oil. It's fucking mad. Why should we pay the bastards?'

'They want all the country's money? The greedy lot, can't they be kind and humane to us?' Shaba asked this as if asking for forgiveness. I was getting fed up with her, but was afraid to say anything.

'Asking a capitalist country to be kind! an imperialist country to be humane! What sweet words, woman! I'm wasting my breath. Bring in the dinner.'

161

I was getting desperate. They had argued amongst themselves, and Father might not want to answer my questions and talk to me about the oil story. He was very thoughtful, as if searching in his mind to solve a puzzle. Mother wasn't interested in the conversation, she was getting Vida ready. She wasn't interested in nationalism or in the political arguments in the paper, only in the accident page. She usually read pieces out loud in which women had been killed, burned to death, beaten up by their husbands or brothers. She would then get very angry, and curse aloud. Father never read the accidents page, he thought it was just like a gossip column.

I crept gently towards my father after the dinner. He had sunk back in his chair and was smoking. I tried once more to pluck up the courage to ask the question again.

'Father, what is oil? Is it what we have in the Aladdin lamp?' He looked up, with a tiny bit of a smile on his face.

'Yes and no. The oil in the cooker is oil, but only one kind. There are many other kinds of oil, like petrol, but they all come from the thick, black oil.'

'Where does it come from? Why does Britain want so much oil? They don't swallow it, do they?'

'Oh no . . .! It is more complex than that . . . let's see . . . I'll tell you the beginning of the oil story. Once upon a time, long ago, a hundred years ago or more, an Australian man found oil in the south of Iran.'

'How? What was he doing there?' I asked him, puzzled.

'Well, we don't know, nobody knows what he was really doing there, perhaps he was a spy. But it is said that he was walking around and suddenly he saw that the land was brown; thick with greasy oil – that was how he discovered it. He wrote to the Shah and asked if he could buy the land and extract the oil, and use it. The oil is very deep down in the earth. The Shah, a useless, ignorant dictator who was always praying to God and marrying new wives and adding to his thousand or more children, didn't know what oil was, or who this man was. He didn't want to know. He wasn't interested. He just replied, "Oh yes, take as much as you like. It's only black oil, and, well, it's dirty anyway." '

'Didn't anyone else say something, like, no, why should you?'

'No, you see he was the Shah and nobody was allowed to say no when he said yes. Anyway, everybody in the government was busy praying to God and marrying new wives, and spending all the country's money on themselves. So after a few years, we don't know

162

how, the British Government told the Shah, "We have the papers you signed, and the oil is ours." '

'How, what does it mean?'

'Well, we don't know, but we can just guess that the Australian, whose name was Darsi, was a British Agent or a spy who didn't want the oil for himself. So either he sold his papers to the British Government or he was one of them.' It was very difficult to understand all these different things. I was puzzled. 'Now,' my father continued – I was still thinking about this Darsi man giving his papers to the British – 'our Prime Minister said, "The oil is ours. We want to save it for ourselves and for our future, and we don't want you to take it and distribute it or sell it." But the British said "No, if you want to keep your oil you must pay us." '

'Are they very poor? Haven't they got any money? Haven't they made enough money out of our oil?' I asked.

'Yes, they have. All these years they have sold our oil and made good money, lots of profit from it. But they want a different kind of money now. It is called compensation, blood money. But the Prime Minister doesn't agree, so the British Government has called on all its friends to boycott Iran and not buy our oil. This means that no country can give food or medicine to Iran. That's why we are very poor nowadays and haven't got much to eat, because there isn't much food in the country. Our trade has nearly stopped.'

'Why? What is the British Navy? Why do they want to fight us?'

'Because Iran is selling her oil to Japan and Italy; the British Government is taking Iran to the World Court, saying Iran is guilty and should be punished. Iran wants some American aid, but President Eisenhower has written back to Mosadegh saying he is sorry but he can't help Iran, unless Iran agrees to Britain's terms. So it's a very difficult time for us. The British Navy is in Iranian waters, perhaps there will be a war soon. They can invade Iran and get rid of Mosadegh.'

'So Britain will make war on us . . . why? . . . because it doesn't want us to eat, to have medicine? Is that so? Why? Why is Britain so cruel, so violent?'

'Well, when you grow up you will learn about it, about capitalism, imperialism, world economy, and many other things. You will be able to read books, newspapers, and listen to the radio. Then you will learn more and more. Read about Marx and Engels, Lenin, our leaders and thinkers, and why capitalism should be overthrown.'

'Come to bed, and go to sleep. You'd better learn the cooking first, girl,' Shaba told me sarcastically.

'Yes, read the books, fine, and batter your wife,' Mother murmured under her breath.

I didn't take much notice of what they said. I was still listening to my father, who was still talking. But I didn't understand what he was talking about, he was using too many big words that went over my head. I would always go blank when my father used such language. I was dozing off. I had enjoyed the oil story, though I couldn't follow the end of it.

Twenty-four

There was one day when Father seemed very happy. He came home waving the newspaper and cheering. 'The Shah has left Iran! Victory is here! hurrah! hey!' I had never seen him so bright and happy, smiling and shouting and glowing with warmth. He was going out to celebrate with his friends, and he ordered his hot water to be made ready for him directly, as he couldn't wait. He must have a toast or two to this occasion. Mother didn't say much but Shaba was annoyed that he was going out with his friends and that they would be drinking our housekeeping money away.

I was playing with my cat's cradle in the living room. Mother didn't let me go out because she wanted to cut and sew my school uniform and she needed me to be around so that she could measure me. Outside in the yard, the sun was ablaze and the heat was exhausting. Shaba was cooking the lunch in the yard and trying hard to do it in the shade. Mother had spread the grey material on the floor with scissors, cotton, and needles near her. She measured the length of my body, around my waist, my chest and hips. She wrote the measurements down and tried to cut the material accordingly. She folded and unfolded the fabric to decide which side to use for the sleeves, and which side for the skirt. She said she must be very careful and save every centimetre because there wasn't enough fabric, and she had to fiddle around hoping that it wouldn't end in a short sleeve or a tight waist as she couldn't afford to buy any more. She cut two long sleeves and spread them on the floor, then she cut the skirt and the upper parts of the tunic and spread them out too. I stopped doing my cat's cradle, untangling my fingers from the string every now and then and watching her. It looked funny, all those pieces of material in the shape of my body lying around on the carpet. I asked her what she was going to do after the cutting, and when I could wear it. She said that she was going to sew it by hand and she didn't know how many days it would take to finish it. So I couldn't even look forward to wearing it soon. Why was everything so slow and unpredictable?

Suddenly Ozra, Sara's mother, opened our front door, and thrust half her body inside. She called to my mother, 'Mina Khanoom! [Khanoom means woman or wife]. There's a big demonstration in Railway Square, everybody is going to watch it, everybody is celebrating the Shah's departure, let's go and see!' Mother stopped her sewing and looked at her, puzzled. I was puzzled too. Ozra didn't often come to call on my mother to do something with her. She was a different kind of woman, a strong, happy, active woman who was always talking with the others in our street, arguing with them. She beat any children who bullied or hurt her own. She stood there and called Mother again. Shaba, who had heard her, said discouragingly, 'Don't waste your time following the men in their folly – they are always demonstrating nowadays, they have nothing else to do. They get a bellyache if you ask them to help you at home.'

'But they are celebrating now, all over the place, they are happy and congratulating each other! Mr Eby is probably with them,' Ozra answered Shaba.

'Yes, I know, he's probably there drinking. Let the men celebrate, it has nothing to do with women except that they are crowding the roads and making it unsafe for us. Don't compliment them by joining them.'

Mother wasn't sure, and told Ozra that the crowded streets weren't safe for women and there wasn't anything interesting there for us anyway. I wanted to go and see what was happening. I was annoyed at what Shaba had said. She was always negative. Father was right when he said that old women always moan about everything. Ozra insisting, Mother packed her sewing and grabbed her chador.

I stood up excited. 'Shall I take my chador too?' I asked my mother. Shaba said 'Yes,' and Mother said 'No'. I wondered which person to follow but grabbed my chador in the end as both women had theirs on too. We left the house with Shaba shouting after us, 'Be careful, don't mix with the men. They are wild with excitement.'

We ran through the narrow alleys. Ozra told any woman we saw on the way, carrying her shopping or her children, to follow us, to come to Railway Square as everything was happening there. 'It is a victory demonstration! We have won! We can have our own government from now on!' Ozra called to the women encouragingly. I was clutching my mother's chador and dragging myself behind them. They took such large strides and mine were so small that catching up with them was hard work. When we had come out of our alley into the main road we saw many more people going in the same direction as we were, towards the square. All the women had chadors on, most of the young girls had them too.

The roads were very crowded; there were many cars, carts, donkeys with fruit on their backs, and people going in every direction. When we reached the little park, we saw masses of men crammed in and around the square. The little park was crowded too, with men running and jumping over its iron fence, treading on the flower beds and rushing into the square. We saw the demonstrators and heard them shouting. We walked faster and faster; as we couldn't climb the fence and take the short cut like the men, it took us longer to get there. We were very excited, dying to see everything from close up.

In the square there was just a tiny corner on the east side, where the tea houses and fruit stalls were, where the women had gathered, standing and watching. The rest of the square and the adjoining roads were full of men and only men. We walked over to the women's side, for Ozra said that we should stand with them. There were rows and rows of men standing around watching. We passed through them and got to the women's section. There we found ourselves places, met some of our neighbours and stood there waiting. People were everywhere, all round, rank upon rank of human figures.

Men were climbing up the trees, the walls, the shop fronts and the park railings. Some were sitting on the roofs, on top of trees, buses and cars; many were hanging out of the open windows of the railway office block and the silo offices on the opposite side of the road. They were all bending down, their eyes fixed on the centre of the square.

The circle in Railway Square was getting more and more crowded, thicker and thicker with people all facing the Shah's statue in the middle and pushing each other. We heard the demonstrators shout, saw their red banners and a lot of Iranian flags. Ozra asked Mother to read the writing on the placards and banners for her.

'Well, there are so many of them, I can't see the little ones. There is one from the Abadan Oil Workers' Union, one from Tehran's Students' Union, one from the Shoemakers' Union, and one saying "We Want the Control and the Profit of our Oil" and "Death to the Shah", another "British and American Imperialism Out" and "Mosadegh is Our Leader". There are more, but I can't read them all, it's too much.'

'What is imperialism?' Ozra asked.

'Men who only care about money. The British businessmen, who only want the oil to make money from it.'

'I don't understand. I thought we only needed the oil for burning, for light, cooking and getting warm. What is that sign then? Who are they?' Ozra pointed to the red banner with pictures of the hammer and sickle on it.

'They are the Communist Students' and Communist Workers' symbols. They don't just want the oil but a lot of other things and communism as well.' Ozra looked quite muddled.

The demonstration grew and the shouts became louder and louder until they were no longer distinguishable. It was very hot and sweaty. It must have been near midday, when the sun is hottest. I was surrounded by the black wall of women's chadors. I could see only chadors and shoes, too boring to look at for long. I was hot and sweating, and getting fed up with the crowd, with the rows of women who pushed against each other. I pulled my mother's chador. 'I can't see anything,' I complained. She didn't answer.

'Mum, I can't see anything.'

'What can I do?'

'I can't see anything and I'm being squashed!'

'Wait, be patient,' was her answer.

'I can lift you up, little girl,' a man said to me. I looked up and saw Mulla and Haji next to each other amongst the women. How had they got mixed up with us? Perhaps because women trust mullas and respect them, they allowed them in our line. I looked at Mother, but she was absorbed in something else. Mulla said it again, 'Little girl, I can lift you up and put you on my shoulder, if your mother allows.' I had never liked Mulla, I didn't trust him, but I was stuck there with nobody else wanting to help me. He looked nice and clean, smiling at me.

Mother just looked at him for a second and I asked her again: 'Please. May I?'

'Yes,' she said, 'but take your shoes off, don't make Mulla's aba dirty.'

I took off my shoes and gave them to Mother. With one hand I held my chador tight under my chin, and with the other I balanced myself on Mulla's hands and was lifted up on to his shoulder. I put my feet there, wobbly at first but firm when he put his hand around my waist and held me there, right above everybody, high in the middle of the sky. I was excited because I could now see from this height everything that was happening around me. The small square was packed with men, perhaps it had never been so crowded in its life. There were heads and more heads everywhere the eye could see, beyond the square in the streets nearby, and the further I looked the smaller the heads became. I could see people, banners, flags, placards with large pictures of Mosadegh. The demonstrators were shouting, 'Victory is ours!', 'Mosadegh is our leader!' and 'The Shah has run away!' It seemed I could hear them better now and understand what they were shouting. The men around the square looked very excited; they were waving their fists in the air, shouting out and wiping the sweat from their faces. They were still facing the Shah's statue. I was hot too, but not as hot as I was when I was standing, even though the sun was now directly burning my head.

Among the red flags I could see some women too, without chadors. Some had school uniforms on, and they too were shouting and waving their fists. All of them looked very hot and excited, and they were wet with sweat. The little square where the Shah's statue was solidly sitting on its marble column was still intact. The neatly planted flower beds around it had geraniums, pansies and roses in bloom. They looked fresh, colourful and beautiful. No one had yet crossed the iron fence, but people were pushing that way all the time. Suddenly I saw a very long, thick rope being handed over the heads of the demonstrators and passed down to the men in the front line by the fence. Soon after, some men jumped over the fence and trampled the flower beds. There were louder and more excited shouts: 'Bring the bastard down! Pull him down!' A few men tried to climb up the marble column but it was too straight and too slippery, and they collapsed. They tried a different method, this time standing on each other's shoulders, making a human ladder and passing the rope up to the man at the top, who managed to find a foothold by the statue and pull himself up. He stood up near the Shah's statue. The crowd cheered and shouted again, 'Pull it down!' He knotted the rope a few times around the Shah's neck and round the horse's legs and neck. The Shah's statue, still unaffected by it all, was smiling and waving his hand. Some more men climbed up and started dismantling the statue with the few tools that they had

168

carried up with them. They were trying very hard, but it wasn't easy. The crowd beneath were gasping and pulling back in case the figure fell and crushed them all beneath its heavy weight. The men were busy bashing and banging away at the hard metal, trying to wrench the statue from the marble column and push it to the ground. It was a hard job and the statue didn't seem to be dismantled so easily.

Everybody was agog with excitement, all eyes were up there, looking intently. I was excited and gasping too. At last the heavy metal figure was dislodged and pushed down amid a gasp and cheers from the crowd. It landed on the ground with a loud bang, and the men slid down from the column. They ran through the flower beds, trampling them under their feet. The crowd pushed forward again and the men started shouting swear words and spitting at the statue, which was still smiling, but at a different angle. Some men started kicking it with their feet, some hurt themselves and withdrew. It was thrilling to be able to see everything as it happened, and I could see much better than anybody else.

The men were still kicking the statue and swearing at the Shah. I had been looking on, comfortable and carefree, without any need to move or change my position. Suddenly I felt uncomfortable. Mulla's hand was fumbling around my waist, under the chador, trying to push my skirt away, touching my pants. I cringed. My body froze. I felt cold and all knotted up. He had pushed my pants down. His hand was moving between my legs. I felt like a stone; I couldn't move, I didn't make a noise, didn't even breathe. All my muscles tensed up, closed up and squeezed inside my body.

His fingers felt like a nail pushing inside my body, injuring my flesh. I thought, 'Open your legs, open them more, it won't go in.' I turned my eyes away from the men around the statue, who had now taken out their penises and were pissing on the hard metal, creating a pool of urine on the soft earth between the statue and the crowd. I didn't know what to do or what to say. Nobody was looking at me. Mulla's hand was covered by my chador, nobody noticed him or what he was doing to me. Everybody was staring at the men who held their pricks in their hands and were pissing on the solid statue. I felt ill, injured and bruised. I wanted to puke on his head. But I was afraid to say anything. I wanted to get down but I couldn't ask.

At home I hid myself, sat in my dark corner, feeling shy and miserable, and didn't say anything to anybody. My body was violated, it was aching and sore. I was afraid in case somebody found out, in case I was beaten. I felt frightened from head to toe. I held my churning stomach in my hands in that dark, safe corner and tried to stay hidden from everybody.

Father walked in, angry and sad, read the news headlines out and started grumbling.

'The victory isn't going to last long – there's a rumour that the CIA is planning to engineer a coup to get rid of Mosadegh and bring back the Shah.' He puffed at his cigarette and read the paper with a melancholy air. Thank God, he didn't notice me and see what had happened to me. Nobody did.

Twenty-five

It was a Friday, the Muslim day of rest, a day like any other, when the soldiers came.

It was Friday morning. The house was quiet, and the sun cooler. The fish were still asleep in the bed of the pond. I went to look for them but decided that I shouldn't wake them up. The yard was cool and empty, the geranium pot on Afagh's stairs in full bloom, full of flowers. I smelt them: they had a strong, sweet scent, delicious to smell. I sat there on the stairs and picked them, one by one, the small fresh shiny flowers. I strung them together to hang around my neck: a geranium necklace.

I went to look at the ants which had tunnelled a hole in the ground the day before. I took some crumbs of bread with me; perhaps they would be out looking for their breakfast. I saw a lonely ant, and put a crumb in its way. She checked it all over with her body: it was too heavy for her to carry. She went back to the hole in the ground and soon appeared again with a long queue of ants behind her. They headed for the crumb in a straight line, then lifted it up all together and carried it back to their home. I teased them a few times, putting the bread crumb down much further away, changing its position; once I put down a dead fly instead; but each time they managed to bring out reinforcements to collect the food and carry it home. I was fascinated by their patience, discipline and collective working; and the fact that they were inexhaustible, searching, building and storing. I was astonished, but at the same time took pleasure in watching them.

I heard the tramp of soldiers' feet. They occupied the narrow alley which ended at our house. The other two houses were barred, and one soldier was stationed in front of each house. Our door was flung open. I stood there in the middle of the yard, stiffening. I felt cold, a marble in my hand dropped to the floor with a loud noise and rolled towards the gutter. I couldn't follow it to pick it up. Grandmother remained hunched by the kitchen door.

The soldiers moved towards the living room. Father, coming out of it, saw them and froze, half bent on the threshold of the living room. Their khaki uniforms looked new, and each of them had a gun and a baton, one on either side of his belt. I closed my eyes and slowly crept backwards step by step, till my back hit the cold wall. I was caught between the triangle of the brick walls. I stood huddled there, terrified, squeezing myself into the tiny corner. The men's batons were hanging, swinging black, stiff and long. One hand on his baton, the other on his gun, the sergeant pronounced stiffly, 'Are you Eby? A machine-operator in the Vank factory?'

Father opened his mouth, but his tongue was stuck. His small blue eyes grew larger and larger, his cheeks sank, his eyes popped out like marbles. His face went white, he looked shocked. He held his pyjama bottoms as if he was cold, insecure. A soldier moved closer towards him. I was afraid they might pull down his loose cotton pyjamas.

'We have found communist papers under your machine in the factory. You're coming with us. Get dressed and packed, fast.'

The soldier moved his baton threateningly, that hard, tarry, ugly object. One soldier moved into the living room. They started to search everywhere. 'Look for books, papers, pamphlets,' one soldier told the others. One of them came towards me. I squeezed my shoulder blades against the brick wall, as if I could press hard enough to vanish through it to the other side. I wanted to melt away, run, but I was stuck there. He stood near me, he was too big, like a monster. He knelt down and looked in my face. I felt his nasty breath, it's stink of smoke. My skin shrank with fear, a cramp whirled round inside my stomach. He smiled, his decayed, black, broken teeth showing. He must have eaten too many sweets, I thought.

'Little girl, can you tell me if you have any books at home?'

'Yee . . . s.'

'Show me where they are.' I walked towards the sitting room, my legs wobbling. He followed closely behind me. My mother, sitting down holding Hamid and Vida tight close to her bosom, stood up, petrified. I pushed at the bundle of mattresses, my hands shaking like a bird in the cold wind. The mattresses were thick, heavy and warm; I wanted to creep into the middle of them and hide there for a long time. They were keenly watching me. I fumbled about and from the dark bottom of the pile I pulled out with my numb hands my books and notebook, and held them out. His eyes shone dirtily, and an ugly smile covered his face; he grabbed them and looked at them. He opened my exercise book, and his face fell as he searched through the rough hand-written lines:

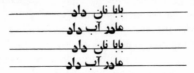

FATHER BRINGS IN THE BREAD.
MOTHER BRINGS IN THE WATER.
FATHER BRINGS IN THE BREAD.
MOTHER BRINGS IN THE WATER.

Ten lines of each on every page. He closed the notebook without losing his temper, came closer to me again and asked calmly, 'Any other books, little girl?' He smiled dirtily again. His open mouth looked like a dried-up, empty well.

'No.' I wanted to puke.

'Are you sure?'

'I don't know . . . I don't know about any other books.' I couldn't hold my head up any longer. My neck was sinking, my stomach whirling like when I was sick and just about to vomit. I leaned on the bundle of mattresses, my eyes going blurred. I trembled, my whole body stopped feeling; I shook my head lifelessly.

He walked away, angry. They searched the rooms, the kitchen, ransacked the corners, Shaba's knapsack, and her old photographs, the treasured pictures of her children, were thrown about. She got mad and pushed one of them and told him loudly, 'Don't be so damned arrogant and careless. Be afraid of God, your power may not last.' A soldier pushed her back: she fell over and just sat there. Father shouted at him, but he in turn was insulted, 'You fucking bastard, commie, red, godless!' They burst into the guest room, and with their dirty boots they walked in on Mother's cleanly swept carpet; one of them forced Mother's closet open. He threw her

172

clothes out, shoved aside her nicely folded sheets and pillow cases. One soldier dug deep into the big wooden safe, took out the silver teacup holders and examined them.

'Hey! real silver! . . . ha . . . real nice . . . rich workers.' We only used them on very special occasions, when we had dear guests. Now they were being invaded. He took two of them and quietly pushed them into his pocket. Mother moved one step forward to protest, then, taken aback, moved two steps backwards.

The sergeant in command rounded the soldiers up. They handcuffed my father, two soldiers holding him on either side, and led him out. He stood firm now, upright, his face had regained some of its colour, he held his head up, looking confident. His eyes were the same old eyes, angry and searching, but they were sad now. He knew that he had to go, and looked unhappy. But he looked at the soldiers with hatred, despising them, as if he wanted to spit on them.

Two soldiers in front went forward and opened the door, and we saw the crowds of neighbours who were watching our house intently. The soldier left our living room, treading on Shaba's photographs which were scattered on the floor. I ran to my mother. Shaba protested to the sergeant, 'What about us? his family? We will have no breadwinner if they take him away. They should have mercy on us and the children!' The sergeant shouted at her that she shouldn't interfere with the law. If he was thinking about the welfare of his family, he shouldn't have got involved in subversive action against the state.

Our alley looked narrower and tighter, with a line of bodies on either side. There were so many eyes on us: it was frightening to be watched by so many. I crept under Mother's black chador, beneath her feet. It was dark, warm and safe. Through a tiny hole I looked out. There was no sound from anybody, only the shoving, the hissing of the crowd, and murmurs of surprise. Mulla stood at the end of our alley at the head of the crowd. In his long, dark robe he looked huge, towering above them. When Father was led to the part of the alley where Mulla was standing, he pointed his finger at him and shouted, 'He is a commie! a trouble-maker! He must have caused another strike . . . Taking him to prison? A better place for him.'

His cold, savage remark was so cruel, his pointing finger hung in the air accusing us; long and stiff like the soldier's baton, like the finger that had forced itself into my body. Sara's mother Ozra couldn't tolerate it any more. She moved forward, saying, 'Oh, shut up, you hypocrite preacher! He is a decent working man, more than you can say for yourself. Why don't they lock you up? It would do everybody good, you liar . . .' A soldier pushed her in the chest against the wall and silenced her.

With their backs to us the soldiers marched on, taking my father further and further away. My eyes were glued to the soles of the soldiers' boots, walking step by step away. He was going, going. I pulled the chador over my head. I couldn't see a thing, I was blind. Beneath the chador it was a tiny small world that was dark, terribly dark, but safe, warm, and a good hiding place. I wanted to stay hidden there for ever.

Twenty-six

I was in a hazy state of confusion. So much had happened so fast that I couldn't work it out. What had the men really been doing in Railway Square? Why had Mulla been nice to me and put me on his shoulder, and then put his finger in my body? Why did the soldiers take Father away? Because he read newspapers and books? But why would he go to prison for that? Although I didn't like my father's bossiness and the way he beat my mother and insulted Shaba, I still missed him.

Shaba was very restless, anxious and sad. She prayed all day long that Father might be released soon. She read the Koran under her breath, and counted the beads on her rosary all the time. Mother looked very worried and disturbed by the whole event. She didn't say much, but the way she looked meant 'as if I didn't have enough troubles already'. Shaba was more openly worried. She went on grumbling:

'I told him. There is no bread in politics. I told him to be careful, not to challenge the government, they're too strong and can crush you. It's a wild world. Go to work, earn your bread, come home to your family. I knew he was getting himself into big trouble. Now what can we do? Three children to feed . . .'

She murmured these words and walked up and down outside the house.

174

A few days passed. We didn't hear from anybody, except our immediate neighbours who came to see and console us. Ozra, Sara's mother, was very kind, and came to see us regularly. Mother thanked her for sticking up for us and saying what she had said to the mulla. She said that sooner or later somebody had to expose him. Our neighbours were very kind and told us that it was not Father's fault, it was the government's, that the Shah was back with the help of the Americans, and Mosadegh was under house arrest; all the opponents of the Shah had been either arrested or were in hiding. They were kind towards us. They brought us food, fresh fruit and sweets, talked to us kindly, and gave us support and hope.

Amo Salim came to see us. He sat down to talk with Shaba and Mother. He was in a bad mood and looked very serious, I had never seen Amo in such a state. I thought he could never be anything but a happy man. He asked Mother what she wanted to do, and offered to take us to his house and look after us until Father came out of prison. Shaba agreed with this. She said that a family needed a man and we should all go to his house. But Mother wasn't so sure.

'I've seen him in prison,' he said. 'Zahedi's military coup and the arrest of Mosadegh have led to his supporters and the communists being rounded up. The leaders are being executed. He doesn't think he will be out so soon.'

'Yes, I suspected that . . . but it is hard for me to decide.'

'You can come and stay with us, or go to your relations . . . wherever you feel most at home.'

'He never thought about his family, about us, he was so callous . . . and he wanted to save the world.'

'It is not his fault he is in jail . . . though he is not without faults either.'

'He wasn't realistic. He didn't care for us, his family. He never gave us enough housekeeping money and made us suffer unnecessarily. He had his head in the clouds.'

'Yes, but he wanted change, he wanted a fair and just government, with better wages for the workers.'

'He wanted communism, Stalin's government here, and he believed that he was always right, a leader.' Mother was bitter and resentful.

'I think he was too hot-headed. He is young and forceful. He didn't stop to think, to see his faults, see and criticise himself.'

'As far as he was concerned he was a man and he was faultless – he knew everything. He had travelled and had seen the fruits of the Russian Revolution . . . my God, he would never accept that he could make mistakes, oh no, not him, the big patriarch.'

'Men are like that, that's his fault, but he had the right ideas. I feel the same about socialism, the right to decent wages, free education and free medical care for all, and the right to choose what *we* want . . . But the problem is really that it just isn't enough having a few people, and a party; we really need thousands more, a few million to really come out and make the same demands . . . we are fighting against such odds, you see.'

Grandmother was preparing the tea and ignoring their conversation as if she didn't care about anything except her son and his freedom.

'But all the demonstrators were men, young men and boys. Those who have no responsibilities at home. We saw them in Railway Square,' said Mother.

Up till then I had been sitting on Amo's knee and playing with his hands, but I suddenly detached myself from him and moved away. I felt the pain of that man's finger in my body. It still made me cringe.

'Yes, you're right. This is bad, but worse, you know, was something I saw yesterday. I saw some of our neighbours who were demonstrating for Mosadegh, out again demonstrating for the Shah! It's really naive to think we can bring about socialism for the people. And Eby was naive too.'

'Men are all the same. They're like children, they don't really know what they want, and they try to impose themselves on everything and everybody. He left us hungry, without shelter, and he beat us. I don't care for his socialism, it doesn't concern me and my children, it's just sweet talk and men are good at it! They're no good at anything else!'

'Mina, you have no worries, you have money, you are educated, you can support yourself, you don't need anybody. You are a strong woman.'

'I don't know if I have any strength left in this house.'

'Yes, you have . . . you want to send your children to school, you forced Eby to agree with you. This is your strength. I admire you and you know that . . . my wife and I cannot afford to send our children to school. She is thinking of sending Akbar, who will be nine soon, to be an apprentice in a factory. We just hope that they will grow up soon and learn skills to earn money. And my daughters . . . we will marry them off soon.'

'I told Eby that we should send the children to school, not to a factory or a husband's bed. But I don't think I can do it any more . . . I can't afford it.'

'Perhaps we should give more to our children,' said Amo. 'In the Soviet Union we learned many things, many skills and ideas, and we thought that when we came back to Iran we would do the same, share it with others and demand the same for ourselves. Soon I realised we couldn't. We couldn't really transfer the Russian experience to Iran – not a handful of us anyway – and expect it to work, not on a hungry belly. I always said to Eby, "A full belly first, then a good health system, then education for ninety percent of our illiterate population." Eby hoped and tried as best as he could, but now it seems that even Mosadegh's attempts at nationalism have failed. We're going backwards now, backwards. Perhaps we will go back in history as far as the Dark Ages, till we can't go back any further.'

'Perhaps the best thing for me to do is to take the children with me and go back to my home town. Perhaps I can have my old job back after ten years.'

'But you don't know anybody there, your father is dead and you've sold the house you inherited from him. You shouldn't have done that. Your relations have moved around and you haven't kept in touch with them.'

'I know. I haven't seen the place for years. Perhaps it has changed so much that I won't recognise it. But it seems the only thing I can do.'

'Mina, if you have made your decision, I won't force you to come and live with us. You know what is best for you. But I will take Shaba with me. She can stay with us until Eby is freed.'

'Will he be executed?' Mother groaned.

'No, it won't happen. Don't think about it. They won't execute people for being a member of a Party, for selling and distributing papers.'

'Won't they?'

'No, don't think about it. It's right for you to go away. Yes, it's the best way, you've made the right decision. You will have the will to do it. That's great. I think the children will be safe with you and be looked after properly. This is a very important step. We need more women like you. I will give you some money for food and for basic things.'

Shaba, with the tea in her hand, had heard the last part of their conversation and protested that she didn't want to be separated from the children. We shouldn't break up our home. But it had never really been a home, and whatever it was, it was already broken up. I had never liked it, it was full of arguments, quarrels, fights and hunger. That was why I was working so hard to go to school.

The summer of 1953 was hot. We were on the road in late Mordad. Mordad – the middle month of summer – is the hottest month, when the roads are scorching. In late Mordad it was supposed to be cooling down, and the autumn air approaching. But the summer of 1953 wasn't like that. Autumn was far, far away. The heat went on.

The sun brings the heat, the hot, boiling, scorching, baking, unbearable heat. The sun is warm, soothing and warm. She shines bright, sending out rays of light, bright yellow light: yellow the colour of hope and growth; yellow the sign of sickness and despair.

The sun is low at dawn and dusk, bright and dim on the horizon. The sun appears and is supreme; disappears, lost in darkness, dissolved in night. The sun is the violence of the day, breaking the peace of the night. She showers dust everywhere, dust in the air, sand in the desert.

The sun is the twin sister of water, they complement one another, are mirrored in each other, the sun and the water, heating up and cooling down, the pleasure of opposites.

The sun is a cover, she is the curtain of the day; a blanket spreading over, taking over, she covers and discovers: the earth, the universe, is hers, is everywhere, is vast.

The sun is the destruction of the night, the calm, peaceful night, the restful, brooding, thinking night. When nature is at rest, before the birth, the night is the dreaming, private, unconscious self, the self in itself, the self in unconsciousness.

The sun is the current, the continuity of flowing streams, continuity in the making. The sun beats down, she is violence, the violence of continuity and perpetuation. She is dominance and unremitting energy.

The sun moves in a circle, coming and going, on and on: repetitious, inescapable. She rises daily, the norm, the ordinary, the matter-of-fact, the banal.

Hers is the kingdom of light, of energy and power. The sun is powerful, too powerful: she overpowers as she pours down a shower of light when she is overhead.

The sun is hard, harsh; a burning fire, a fiery temperament; she is vitality, life itself, life-giving; she it is who grants existence, birth, growth and energy for living.

But she is also destruction, sweat, corruption; she is the desert with its dearth of water, of precious water. She is death and she is decay, the stinking corpse, its foetid smell, the black water with its flies, bugs and buzzings; with flies over shit, flies everywhere, shit everywhere.

The sun is one, one is God, one is tyranny, one is all in one, negation of all, one is oneness, one in unity.

The sun is the day, the sun is life, growing and living. The sun on the earth, shining on nature, creates and produces: ripens fruit, makes flowers blossom; corrupts fruit, kills flowers. She makes the plants grow, and lets them die, and the trees and the crops. She makes the wild seasonal fruits to grow, and the plants and the crops.

The sun wakes you up, sends the women to the fields, clothes them in black, in dull, artificial black. The sun is heat and sweat, the enemy of the labourer on the road. She makes you warm and relaxed, sleepy and passionate, angry and crazed. The sun slows you down, sends you to sleep in the afternoon, makes you tired and thirsty. She tans you, blackens you, makes you brown, makes the beautiful dark colour of the skin.

The sun is Mithra the Goddess of light, the Goddess of energy, of fertility and love: our ancient religion worshipped the Goddess of the sun.

The sun is desire, the desire for nakedness, for passion and love; for physical love, human love, human passion, for the passion of creation and the passion of birth, for vital love.

But in the land of the sun, in the land of Mithra, there is no love, no passion, no nakedness nor smiles, human touch nor contact, nor free human relationships; but only *Islam*, its laws and legislation, its binding rules and the controls which chain us, which chain us always, to death, punishment, lashes, and stonings, to black coverings for women and men's violence against women; and to the perpetuation of that violence.

The sun is the cycle of life, growth and death in the land of Mithra; waste and productivity, waste and creativity, and full human potential.

We were on the way to Mother's home town. Shaba had gone off fearfully to Amo's house, and we had packed a small bag and were on the road.

We had locked up our rooms and asked Afagh to look after them for us. When we were saying goodbye to Afagh she looked sad: I was surprised, I thought she would be glad that we were going, because she wouldn't have any problems with us any more. But Afagh looked sad: she gently touched my hair and Hamid's and told us to be good children and help our mother.

'I always resented this marriage of yours, I knew it would end in this sort of way.'

'But how did I know? Show me a woman with a good marriage and a happy ending? Tell me, is it you? me? Shaba? Which of us?'

'Yes, all right, forget it and try to concentrate on a new life, a better life for yourself.'

'Yes, I'll try at a better time. How can I at a time like this? So much happening . . .'

They both had tears in their eyes. They kissed and hugged in a sisterly way, and said farewell. I was still puzzled that Afagh cared.

Mother was carrying Vida, who was now too heavy to be carried in her arms for a long time. Hamid and I were clutching her, one on each side of her chador. When we passed our lane – with our heads down to avoid the neighbours – I said goodbye to my friends, Sara, Farideh, and Shahin: my best friends. Leaving them and our street was the first painful taste of exile in my life.

Mother said that from our house to her town it was two hours' drive on a coach, but we had to go through Tehran by bus and get a coach in the outskirts, because it would be much cheaper. We got into the bus, which took us through the crowded streets, squares, and shopping markets, past Rey's slum housing estates and the cement factory, and rode through the busy areas of the holy shrine of the Shah-Abdol-Aziz. We got off the bus in the holy square where the constant bustling never ended, and walked through the crowd, passing the golden shrine, to the outskirts of Tehran.

Although it was the end of the month and supposed to be cooling down, it was still hot, especially when walking under the sun on a dusty road. We were heading for Kashan city, where the best Persian carpets come from, Mother's pride and joy, the beautiful work of women artisans. We were also passing another holy shrine, the holy shrine of Masomeh, the sister of the eighth Imam, which was in the holy city of Gum. Mother hoped that our coach wouldn't stop in the city, would just pass through it without any delay. Stopping there for women was problematic, as men ordered them to hide themselves more, not to eat, or feed the baby in public.

We were now on a long, narrow road. 'I'm tired, and it's just the beginning, just the beginning of the road,' Mother complained, and shifted Vida to her other arm. She was murmuring under her breath.

'The road is too long, there might be nobody at the end of it . . . ten years is too long, who'll remember me? What if I find nobody and no teaching job to go to?'

We were walking along the pavement when we noticed a woman carrying two children in her arms, coming towards us.

'Excuse me, I've left the holy city of Gum and am going to Tehran. Could you tell me which direction to take? A short cut to Tehran? I'm not familiar with this area.'

'We've come from there. Look, take this road and walk straight on. Don't go through the holy square of Rey town. It's a long way, but you're going in the right direction.'

'Thank you very much. I don't know this area at all. Can you tell me if I could get a job easily once in Tehran? I was told there are more jobs there than anywhere else.'

'But not for women . . . I think you can if you try hard. But it's a big city with many vultures. Yes, the capital of injustice. Be careful, and good luck.'

We said goodbye to her and walked on.

'She looked like a beggar. I thought she wanted money,' I told my mother.

'She wasn't. She's looking for work . . . what a task, trying to find a job!'

A newspaper boy crossed the road and came towards us, shouting:

'Today is Kyhan, your daily is out! Full of good news! American Economic Aid to Iran Soon! President Eisenhower Promises Letter to the Shah! . . . Read the Shahanshah, His Royal Highness' speech! His Majesty the Shah of Iran!'

Mother pushed the newspaper offered to her away with disgust and spat on the ground. Not only did she look sad, but sick too.

She started reciting some poetry under her breath. She was like that – for every occasion she had a poem in mind. I could hear only half-snatches of the poem clearly, which she repeated many times with a marked seriousness.

بخت خواب آلود ما بیدار خواهد شد مگر

'Will ever our slumbering fate rise from its deep sleep?'

181

I held Mother's hand clasped in mine. Her small, fat hand with its tiny fingers and hard knuckles held my little fingers tight in its grasp. Her hand was wet with sweat, her veins full of blood beating fast, and she clasped me with a warm pressure. I was holding on. It was a feeling of security, assurance and warmth.

We walked on under the sun till we were exhausted, and could go no further. Here we were on the pavement of a road which was narrow and unending. We had seen the crowds, the people, the markets, slum buildings and refuse tip of the town. Now on both sides of the road there were vast areas of bare land, uncultivated and empty. No sign of life anywhere, just the sun beating down, dust and flies. Nothing more. The only sign of life was the long line of the asphalt road, and the occasional noise of cars which broke the dead silence.

Hamid and I sat on the edge of the road next to Mother, and we started to thumb a lift. The long narrow road looked endless, and the sun was heating it up. At the end, where the sky met the road, there seemed to be nothing but a wide, endless horizon.

Glossary of Farsi (Persian) Words

aba – surplice worn by a Muslim priest

abgosht – a traditional working-class stew of meat, chickpeas and
    other vegetables

aftabeh – can for carrying water

Amo – paternal uncle

aragh – spirit, a type of vodka

Ayeh – passage taken from the Koran

bimeh – limited form of medical insurance, for civil servants,
    factory workers, etc.

chador – the long, engulfing shawl that covers women from head to
    toe and is held in place under the chin with one hand. The
    imagery throughout the book of the black chador and the black
    veil is symbolic of women's oppression in Iran.

Daie – maternal uncle

dasteh – religious demonstration

Farsi – Persian language

Haji – meaning 'holy' – used to describe someone who has visited
    the pilgrimage centre of Mecca

hammam – public bathing room

havoo – women in polygamous marriages call each other 'havoo'

Herzhe Tudeh – the Communist Party of Iran

hoze – small pond situated in the courtyard of the Iranian house

kiseh – a rough flannel

Majales – the Iranian lower parliament

Mulla – Muslim priest

rial – Iranian coin, a penny

rozeh – sermon

sanak – bread

siegheh – Islamic temporary marriage

sofreh – a cotton cloth spread on the floor to eat from

tadic – the brown fried rice taken from the bottom of the cooking
    pan

tileh bazi – a game of marbles

Chronology of the Struggle to Nationalise Iranian Oil 1950–53

The struggle to nationalise Iranian oil – that is, to wrest it from British control – was a turning point in the history of modern Iran. More than any other issue, this struggle helped to radicalise the Iranian people, and created a mass popular front such as did not arise again until the Revolution of 1979.

1950		Ten imprisoned leaders of the Tudeh (Communist) Party escape from jail.
	April	Mohamed Mosadegh re-elected to the Majales.
	June	Mosadegh launches attack on Prime Minister Ali Razmara.
	November	Mosadegh tables a motion in the Majales for nationalisation of Iran's oil.
1951	March	Prime Minister Razmara is assassinated.
	April	Mosadegh appointed Prime Minister.
	May 1	80,000 demonstrate outside the Majales in support of Mosadegh.
		Motion on nationalisation of oil passed by Majales.
		British navy comes to Persian Gulf to 'safeguard British nationals' in Iran.
		Mosadegh and his supporters occupy the Majales.
		Oil workers go on strike. Army intervenes and fires on strikers, many killed. Martial law is declared.
	July	Averell Harriman, Foreign Policy adviser to President Truman, arrives in Iran to negotiate an oil contract with Mosadegh. Massive demonstrations oppose a new contract on im-

perialist terms, the army fires on the demonstrators and many are killed or injured.

September   Mosadegh takes over Iranian oil industry from the Anglo Iranian Oil Company.

Britain's Labour Government reacts with a boycott of Iranian oil; and complains to the United Nations.

October   Mosadegh goes to the United Nations to defend Iran's new oil policy.

British Labour Government defeated in elections: Conservative Government replaces it.

1952   US President Truman refuses economic aid to Iran in support of Britain's claim to Iranian oil.

June   Mosadegh goes to the World Court at The Hague to defend Iran's position against British complaint.

He resigns as Prime Minister after disagreement with the Shah over the Shah's personal control of the army, which he argues is unconstitutional.

The Shah appoints a new Prime Minister. Massive demonstrations follow, against the Shah and the new government. The army is brought in, tanks roll through the streets and 70 people are killed, many more wounded.

An Italian ship carrying oil from Iran is arrested by British colonial authorities in Aden.

July   Mosadegh once more appointed Prime Minister.

1953 January   3000 shoemakers go on strike. Textile workers join them. 30,000 quarry workers demonstrate.

March   Attempted coup against Mosadegh – his house is attacked but he escapes safely.

The Chief of Police, a Mosadegh supporter, is murdered.

August   Ashraf, twin sister to the Shah, meets American intelligence agents in Paris and Switzerland. £19m changes hands in preparation for a coup to oust Mosadegh.

The Shah flees Iran for Iraq, and then Rome.

Fazlottah Zahedi, an army officer who had been imprisoned by the Allies during the Second World War for his Nazi sympathies, leads a coup against Mosadegh, who is arrested and jailed.

The Shah returns. Zahedi becomes Prime Minister.

Martial law follows, and thousands are arrested and imprisoned, hundreds executed.

Sir Anthony Eden, then British Foreign Secretary, later wrote about the coup: 'The news of Mosadegh's fall from power reached me during my convalescence, when my wife and I, with my son, were cruising in the Mediterranean between the Greek Islands. I slept happily that night.' (Anthony Eden, *Full Circle*, 1960, p 237)